From Arthur's Seat Volume VIII
University of Edinburgh
School of Literatures, Languages and Cultures
50 George Square
EH8 9LH

Published in 2023

Design and typesetting by Salvör Sólnes
Illustrations by Raine Bracken, Alice Eaves,
Kinslee Sikes & Salvör Sólnes

Typeset in PS Fournier

Printed in the UK

http://www.fromarthursseat.com/

CONTENTS

Prose

Excerpts

Letter from the Editors

Dear Reader,

We are delighted to present to you the eighth volume of our annual anthology, *From Arthur's Seat*. It is an in-house project entirely produced by the MSc Creative Writing cohort at the University of Edinburgh. This year's anthology comprises a medley of pieces by writers and poets from various parts of the world. It has been an absolute pleasure to be able to curate and compile their brilliant work into the book that you now hold. We were blessed with a wonderful team and we would like to thank each and every one who gave their best for this project.

From our editors and copyeditors who helped polish and fine-tune each piece, to our art team who created the beautiful cover and illustrations within, to our marketing team who helped raise funds, generate interest locally, and organise events across the city; and last but not least, we would like to give big thanks and a warm hug to our managing editors, Olivia Duff and Zain Rishi, who were a constant support throughout this massive endeavour. As well as a special thank you to Ryan Van Winkle and Patrick Errington; their guidance and encouragement was essential in bringing this anthology to fruition.

We hope you enjoy reading this book as much as we enjoyed producing it.

Happy reading to you!

Editors-in-Chief,
Rasika Bhale and Austin Crowley

Foreword

Dear Reader,

This book can be read anywhere you are, you just need to bring yourself.

If you can, make a cup of tea, crack a beer, let the wine breathe. Drink a glass of water – it's important to stay hydrated and comfortable.

If you are on a train, the tracks' squeak & rattle will make an excellent soundtrack.

If you are in the trunk of an old, dead tree, you'll have consolation from the words within.

If you are in the kitchen, read a story as the dough proves.

If you are being stalked by vultures, this book will distract you and protect you from the sun.

If you have brought us to the loo instead of your phone, we are honoured.

If you are on a boat, we too have been between places.

If you are in a cafe, a poem between nibbles of sponge.

If you are in space, these words will float with you. Some will return you to the ground, some will send you out further.

If you are in bed, forget the day, the cold beyond the blankets.

If you have ever stood by a departure board and thought about all the places you could go, this book is for you.

If you don't like to start at the beginning, you can pick a page. Thirty-four emerging authors have new stories and poems for you.

If you prefer to start at the end & have worked your way backwards, thank you for reading.

You can stay as long as you like and, please, pop by any time you're in the neighbourhood.

Welcome to *From Arthur's Seat*. Wherever you are, we hope you'll enjoy it here.

Ryan Van Winkle
Writer in Residence,
University of Edinburgh

POETRY

I just wanted to feel sad and alone at the seaside but it ended up being shit

C. T. Hilton

"Never feel sorry for a writer.
They're so good at doing it for themselves."

Tom Pow

The seaside is supposed to be the perfect
place for loneliness and heartache; where I
come to hear the waves crash against
the rocks and feel the wind burn the soft

skin of my lips. Where I can sigh into solitary
fish and chips, as I lean on the harbour
wall, watching fishing boats idle in
and feel the world's weight on my shoulders.

But I cannot stand and stare at waves today—
the tide is out by the time I arrive,
and I will not walk across the sinking sands
just to hear the ocean's roar. The wind blows

hard, and the pages of my notebook are blown
back and forth; my fingers are so numb
I cannot hold my pen, and I abandon all
attempts to write whilst sitting on the beach.

When I stand and wait in line at the chip shop, I stamp
my freezing feet and blow warm air into my cupped hands;
upset to see that a fish dinner now costs fifteen fucking quid,
lamenting at how long it's taking for them to serve me.

How can it take twenty minutes to dip a fish in batter and fry the fucking thing!
Finally, having been served, I'm down at the harbour, just trying to enjoy my lunch
but I burn the roof of my mouth because the chips are scalding hot; it blisters and my
tongue will not leave it be; it keeps on prodding at the sore that's filling up with pus.
And as I look about the harbour, there are no fishing boats to see – Brexit was the final blow
to an already crippled industry. And now, of course, the sea-gulls are gathering all around me,
having spied my fish and chips; they are not deterred by my manic, flapping arms – they refuse
to leave me be. Their mocking cries ring out around the empty harbour as the circle closes in.

I realise I am outnumbered and decide to let them fight over what remains of my depressing
fish and chips. I leave, frustrated, and stomp around the backstreets of this quiet seaside town,
feeling much aggrieved that the world will not indulge my desire for aesthetic sadness, until
I turn a corner and see this dilapidated church that's crying out to me in all its crumbled beauty

the sun breaks through the clouds
to kiss my face as I wander, untethered
in this churchyard where even the
gravestones have given up and collapsed.

but as I leave I learn that even this sad backdrop is too much to ask for; a little sign
informs me that the parish council have deliberately collapsed the gravestones
to ensure they do not fall on unsuspecting visitors.

5 A.M. at Dryden House

C. T. Hilton

The light at this hour is gentle, as the soft grey-purple
of elderly night embraces the young blue dawn.

Dew and drizzle meet, mix their dampened bodies
in communion as whimpers of the day's
coming sky are streaked above our heads
where faint wisps of cloud entwine,
moving in a rhythm oblivious to the chill.

It is now the bleary-eyed hours of a Sunday morning;
the soles of our shoes are well-caked in mud,
and our trouser hems are clogged and wet.
The wine that soaked our tongues has seeped away
fogging up our heads, drying out our mouths.

But that is all tomorrow's news,
and the steel train tracks of the city,
with their doom and gloom and
Monday morning emails,
cannot touch us whilst we're lying
on this blanket taken from the sleeping house.

The night's revelries, no longer burning bright,
still spread a warming glow upon this quiet corner
of the field lying fallow next to Harper's Brook,
who gently joins our tender conversation
that warbles, senseless as the song-bird's cry.

Holding each other, we fight off sleep,
not yet ready to let this morning slip
into just another story of something we once did.

Postcard for Isacco
C. T. Hilton

It is cold and loud and wet
in London. Everything is grey.
I have to think
about that night in winter,
stood with you
hand in hand,
above Baleal Beach.
The tide rolled in below us,
deepening the gaps between
the limestone cliffs.
Our shadows stretched
out huge beneath the moon
then shrank as the day pushed in.

Something Very Gentle
Oona MacKinnon-Hoban

Life falls from the rafters
and collects in the woodgrain,
      drifts out to sea on a fishing boat, unmoored
and dark blue in the last warm nights of summer.
Out here past the trees,
      death does not seem such a frightening thing,
where the sandpipers gather in huddles
and the impression of the waves remain in the sand
      long after the tide has gone out.

Wedding Day
Oona MacKinnon-Hoban

Soon my brother will walk through the door,
a married man, and I will look at him
from the same position
I looked at my father
when he came home to tell me
my mother wasn't the type of person
they would try to save anymore.

She died three days later
lying on the couch, tucked under a blanket,
weighing no more than a child would.

That blanket disappeared,
along with the couch.
We have new furniture now,
a different shade of paint on the walls,
a photo above the mantle that wasn't there before
of the row of benches in Central Park
where I sat and cried
thinking of the fact I would never
go grocery shopping with her again.

It is a beautiful day.
Ceramic dishes are all returned.
Bouquets pass across the coffee table.

I am comforted that the flowers
will return to the earth with no impression,
as if no one had bothered to bring them at all.

When spring comes,
I will not expect a resurrection,
but maybe another birth.
Something to make it all new

again.

Little Bird
Oona MacKinnon-Hoban

I saw a little bird perched outside
my kitchen window and thought,
What a mess we've left behind.

Is there room at the table
for the unforgivable fathers?
A place set aside for the women
who loved them?

On another morning,
I will stop seeing closure
as an impatient figure
lingering by the doorframe
and begin to imagine it
as trash bags full of bottles,
the sink overflowing with plates
from the meals we shared.

Out there in the yard,
I see its wings flutter up
over the golden bough
and I plunge my hands
into the dirty water.

For Cruelty's Sake
Alessandra Heitmann

My hair is wet and dripping this morning
on the drive to school
when we hit every red light.
Might as well just go back home.
There will be no learning today.

Water drips onto my upper lip.
I lick it off, counting
the bicycles we pass
like the minutes I wasted
in the shower before we left.

Mom knocking,
       pounding,
              yelling at the door,
I'll carry you to school if you need me to!
But I'll do it myself, I will
swim if I have to, just stop.

I am carsick in the front seat,
my stomach dripping down my chin.
Mom hands me a napkin.
I wring out my hair.
We keep driving.

A fly in the corner
hurls its sorry little body
against the window
but it doesn't break.

That poor bug can't escape
this vomit-scented, water-drenched car
that just keeps going.
He throws himself
again and again and again,

pausing now for a rest.
In that moment
I slam down my palm,
turn his beady body into blood
and wipe my hand on my thigh.

Piñata
Alessandra Heitmann

The problem is
brown hair dyed blonde
falls out in fistfuls.

You grab it in clumps,
just a little kid armed with a bat,
always breaking.

I empty myself everywhere,
let the rushing in of chaos and
fingers
pull me apart.

My brown hair is dyed blonde,
and you finally kiss me
without a cover story.

You've always wanted this.
Reach in. Grab what you came
for.
I'm wide open and waiting.

Visiting Hours
Alessandra Heitmann

It is five o'clock in this hospital room.
Skin-covered people marked

with scars litter the hallways
under a faint gloom of antiseptic.

There are no skeptics welcome here,
only those who aren't afraid

to take a deep breath in
and then let it all out in a scream.

Just plug your ears, love,
and take off those damn gloves.

This thing we have isn't catching.

Blow Me
Kate Genevieve

He asks,
What do you like?

I avoid the question.
Never had time to consider it.

Too busy twisting
into positions.

Balloon animal.

Beelzebub's Tea Party

Kate Genevieve

blood drips down my groin.

you can't be sure
that's the last of it.
to be safe you don't approach
my body but say

> hey, what about me?
> you have hands, after all.

I once covered them
in liquid glue,
peeled
to reveal child palms.

semen between fingers
dries different.

almost empty.
spine slouched,
cup fingered out,
boiled.

might have soup for dinner.

The Empty Space Where I blamed Myself For My Rape
Kate Genevieve

January 31, 2015

....

Sorry

I'm a dick

Got a little too drunk last night

Still putting the night together lol

No its on me

Her Warmth
Yasmine Bridge

If you need shelter, she's got no more.
The for-nows are spent.
If you wanna dip in her pond
consider it drained—

but you claimed
it's *not that deep*
when you're in her deep.

She didn't wanna bash you
but she's been bashed by your bang
one
two
too many times.

She showed you out
but you made yourself wait.
She is a cavity
and her walls are ribbed,
her property comes with an *insulated interior*.

She knows her part
but not what comprises her parts.
Her bed is a stage.

When you were done, she longed for her mother.
But you had another reservation
Slot-in
Booking cancelled
Amended

and yet, despite it all

she could not keep you from your cold.

Otherhood
Yasmine Bridge

I am becoming
reminiscent of the umbilical cord
as I feel my empty belly button

I am becoming
aware of my own breasts
and their lopsided folds

I am becoming
fucked up in the most pretentious of ways
I read Larkin now

I am becoming
an almost adequate imitation
of correctness

I am becoming
the worrier armed with
extra layers and flat shoes

I am becoming
the forehead creases
and the odd grey hair

I am my mother.

Parkinson's
Yasmine Bridge

I clung to your arm
with unknowing regularity.
Our grip was mutual—

this is the natural progression.
This is the condition
and I am conditioned
to hold *you* from now on,

your turn to cling now
with hands which
can no longer
grip at all.

A European Robin

Austin Crowley

Beyond my moss-covered window
the bones of November reach for heaven.
A pinprick of color in the tangle:
a crooning auburn leaf.
But leaves don't sing in autumn.

It is the breast of a jolly robin atop a tree's bare finger.
Flitting to and fro,
she colors the air with her voice,
lifts the world with a trill,
and reminds me that life is not so heavy.

It's time I join her song.

Did I Tell You About The...?

Austin Crowley

Onset, he's got early onset.
You know, haven't you noticed the onset?
He's got it, early.
We have to watch for the signs.

Tin-headed knitting needles
click in the background like words
hidden behind my tongue.

Inside me curls a forbidden question
which stokes a half-choked inhalation;
I feel the tacky clack of my dry epiglottis.

Did I-did *he* overstay his time?

He doesn't like to touch or be touched anymore.

He's so alone now with his onset.
His ruined hands sew failure
and shake with his fury.
Early onset, sunset in rouge.

Dad, I want you to meet Earlie Onsette.

A eulogy for our father:
It's been a pleasure to whine
at your feet all these years.
Marking our brows with ash and singing along
when days weren't so full of rust.

The stories he told me fade away
like warm breath on a mirror.
I tried to bottle them,
but it set in too soon.

A raindrop crawls
down a window,
swells at the lip,
then falls.

Aspirate
Austin Crowley

My gut tells me to cancel my plans,
to cancel all plans,
to remain indoors,
mewling like a baby
in my sticky humid den of retrogression.

Coiled like twine around the neck of a rice wine gourd,
my gut regurgitates itself and slithers out of my spiny body
into a dull paper bag of dust and lice molt.
It murmurs, *Be warm, sublime, and mummify.*

My gutless body is an iris fading to white.
Cataracts build beneath my thoughts and push
through my flesh until I am a pillar of calcified fears;
unmarred and slick like a cave of forgotten dreams.

My ancestors howl and writhe with fury.
They look down upon me, disgust winking
in their eyes at this weakling of a son.
So be it.

I am an ending.

Through the Steep Mountains
Tian Zehua 'Sarah'

People push past you on both sides.
The mountain just leans backwards,
Lets you see,
Lets you breathe close to it.
That green is not life.
It's like coal or iron,
Glistening with a dim lustre,
Bringing ancient death and collapse to an eternal height.

Halfway up in the fog,
With each step,
You can only believe that
The road ahead is brighter
Because the infinite slope
Is replacing your eyes
And catching your falling toes
Again and again to tell you
Time is like a hawk.
Now it flies against the soles of your feet,
Only in charge of the mottled earth beneath.
You will finally enter its cave
Like spinning into the back of the sky.
The winds that once passed through its wing,
Will they be there rummaging around
In the dead feathers and limbs?

You climb senseless
With those stone walls feasting greedily on your traces.
Any part of this place that had been set foot on
Still remains private to you passionately.
You have no idea about
a nutlet, a water source,
Why are they in those positions?
Or a cry, why does it stop so abruptly?

You are lost in the unfinished,
Looking for known memories.
The ruined fortress,
The echo of the cavity,
A gigantic creature in ancient books
With a big head and a short tail.
Until you find out,
Out there in the thin air,
Any sound will be forgotten.
Quietly,
Turning quieter,
Just as the sound of those footsteps
When you came up to the summit.
Then you feel the weight of your body
Disappear
And become a burst of starlight,
Defeat the mountain's skin,
Attached to this pile of bones and roots within.

Room
Tian Zehua 'Sarah'

You'll notice
Dusty Windows.
Everything on the periphery,
A room that is hard to shape.
Maybe languages will die here
Because little notes can't be passed.
But not the same as dreams,
Which will fly across all events.

Then let the sound of the dark waves
Take the names of the birds,
For what they beat off
Is just dust of the earth.
Then bite open familiar fruits
Without any recollection,
And all that flows out
Is a flying river

Falling from deep in the sky
And once reversing a desert.
Overwhelming tastes of freshness and astringency
Are stir-fried on all the human senses.
But who will remember *your* taste
If they are locked back
Into the womb again
With no more disturbance?

So I bite open my tongue
And let out my mother's blood,
Expressing myself from what is not mine.

Curtain
Tian Zehua 'Sarah'

TV shows teach people to imitate
But don't teach people to escape.
In contrast, sunlight never weaves
A dense encoded net when it
Penetrates through meshes.

The clowns are on duty to lift the edge of the world,
And the rest
Fear and expect at the same time
The falling of the crimson curtain
To leave the spectators waiting.
Looking around in the light rain
And finding nowhere to focus,
Thus allowing the ones at the first row to be narrators.
They interpret to the rear rows
What happened on the dancing floor.
Cocktails made of piano melodies,
Colorful dreams and cooled stories.
Slight clank of the triangle, a mosquito buzz,
Or the funeral bell of an unknown hero
Whose amplitude deforms as it spreads,
Causing hundreds of imaginations to be extracted
And stuffed into the interval of rain.

Until
It rains cats and dogs,
And the soaking sunset
Suddenly raises its head in horror.
The death of spectators has crept
To the last row
While the stage is reborn.

Phoebe's Monologue
Olivia Calderón

Let me speak of the tides.
How the three faces
of the moon that bear my name
do not pull, but watch.

Salted seas shift around the world.
Up and down, in and out.

Each appear in cyclical phases,
wrapping around the skies,
just like I first taught them to.

The Atlantic knows no peace.
Vengeful winds transform
to hurricanes, always inciting
its choppy waters to violence.

My granddaughters call to me,
saying there are better bodies
of briny water — the North Sea,
where the water is the temperature
of a moonbeam.

So I heed their summons.

Whales do not
know of the moon,
but every month she
pools in their marble eyes
to gaze upon the world.

The Oracle at Delphi
Olivia Calderón

i still have nightmares about you.

hundreds of reptilian eyes
blinking away the frost of age
just to watch me paralyzed

with the dread that only
my subconscious can dredge up.

stained incisors glint in
irradiated light as you drag
yourself closer, scales *screeching*
against the ice below.

your claws hook into a skin,
a human one, hollowed out
like a dog's chew toy.

you shove every bulge into
that thin tan build, covering every
eye but the two brown ones, squelching

echoing throughout the cavern,
and when every gelatinous part
is completely sealed up,

it's just you. the rainbow
choker the sweater vest the dimple
on your left cheek — it's all you.

there is nothing more terrifying
than one who hides in plain sight.

Coffee Angel
Olivia Calderón

You show up in your purple coat
and molten blue eyeliner
like the main character in a film
that's about to become my favorite.

Soplete, they say when you play checkers
the Cuban way. You move your queen piece
all the way across the board in one move
to win the whole thing.

You played the long game.
Between those blue eyes
and that Polish vodka,
I crumbled like sand.

You win, you win, you win.

Making Salad from Human Remains
Alice Eaves

First, we're going to
switch out those yucky toms
for some lush, beefy toes. Dice them
rough, crack, grate, however you want.
Now we're going in with the lettuce—
I mean lungs. Nice and thin,
the knife should glide right through
just like warm butter.

Okay. Oil, pan, onto the hob
and we're going to fry those breasts.
Make sure you're flipping them over
after a few minutes, we don't want to burn
the nipples here. Can you smell that? *Urgh delish.*
Off the heat and onto that lovely tossed, tossed...salad!

Right. Onto the dressing. Now,
this is where you can get experimental.
I usually mix a good helping of
mayonnaise with capers, a little
dill and lemon. But the real key for me
to balance a dressing is a bit of
blood. The neutral ph level just
really brings the flavours together.
Keep it whole and squeeze
like an old dish rag until all that lovely
juice comes out. Honestly,
such a simple addition
and it just elevates.

For the final touch, sprinkle
with a healthy handful of dandruff.
Any will do. I like something extra
mature, usually male over 70, but
it's really down to personal taste.
And there you have it!
A protein-packed take on a classic.

Weightlessness
Alice Eaves

I've had to reinvent myself too many times
peeled back layer after layer

onions / artichoke / baby gem lettuce
each as threadbare as the next

bugs between my leaves
worms / lice / hungry maggots

forcing me to strip another off
gossamer futures slip away

snakes / gators / blue belly lizards
find strength in their fresh skin

why then do I whimper at the thought
of no more husk to shuck?

what is so terrifying about reaching the
stump / core / ivory bone?

when this is where we all end
just some pulp
                mulch
                      dust in the canopy
                                high above the urban jungle

Braindead
Alice Eaves

We live between paper walls

    bodies wrapped in cling to sweat secrets out

    jellify thoughts   make membrane jam

    macerated   and slipped over sourdough

these walls only get thinner

putty brains simmered to

our only remnant of individualism

Vietnamese summer rolls   slices of cerebrum wedged between beansprouts and avocado

the autumn harvest is continual plucking   limbs pulled up at the root

taken to market and sold to the shadiest bidder   with the biggest wallet

they ply hot cookies down our throats   buttered burnt and unrelenting

    we're so full we cry

Virginia Slims in the Freezer
Kinslee Sikes

It's glaring, it's glaring—
his cigarette monkey
who hangs from the ceiling
and peers down at me.
I think he's always been there.

When I was seven and a pageant queen,
he locked me in a dressing room
because I couldn't stop crying.
He's hit me with a phone,
other times with his small hand,
but he's only burned me once.
Is a monkey responsible for his cigarette ash?

Although, he also held me
when I was living in my car.
Brushed the knots out of my hair,
rubbed lotion on my face,
told me I was clever.
When I subsisted off
prepackaged diet meals
and glossy dolphin posters,
he took me to therapy each week
because he thought it would help.

I still had to retrieve his cigarettes
from the freezer every evening.
I don't know if anyone has ever loved him back
besides me.

Quietly, I watch him try on wedding dresses.
Chiffon bodice, red silk ribbon
around the middle to elongate the torso.
He looks good for his age.

I've seen movies, read books—
it seems no one has a monkey so cruel as mine.

girls weekend sharing SSRIs
Kinslee Sikes

I'm left here alone in my body
and the Hollywood ache comes back
dazzling and glamorous and murderous
my slim hollow fills me
faster and faster
a paralysis
to rival all
zeroes

the dank void tastes of nothing—
no salt, no cream, no cherry filling
no blood, no iron, no small intestine
no centipede, no dust bunny, no sweat

I am
I am
I am

and I take it away

a horse hoof on the throat

larping as my papa
Kinslee Sikes

I wear a jockstrap
and nothing else
to bed

my stomach is
round
hard
large
inflexible

I've eaten bear meat only once
my favorite treat
being cow tongue

I watch old westerns on TV
notice what shooter the cowboy has
feel my toes twitch in my boots
remember the horse that saved my life
six decades ago

my mind could never release
waking up at five in the morning
to feed the beasts
as I try to make each second
not a waste of my goddamn time

I used to tell the grandkids
on Christmas Eve
that Santa didn't like milk and cookies
all he really wanted was beer and pretzels

and when they went along with it
I made each one a blowgun
out of old PVC pipes
I think their ammo was marshmallows
maybe chunks of potatoes—
the dog always fucking ate it up

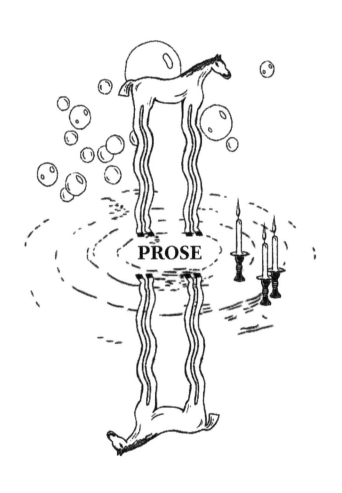

PROSE

Out-of-Towners

Felix Foote

I saw him one October day when I was in the sitting area of Waverley Station, where people settle into uncomfortable metal seats and kill time with books they picked up at the nearby WHSmith before their trains arrive. I, however, wasn't there to join the communal hellish depression of letting the minutes run out. I had walked for ten minutes to the station just to pick up a Too Good to Go bag from the Pasty Shop. As much as Edinburgh, and the UK in general, had insulted my taste buds in a few respects, I had developed an intense love for meat pies and Cornish pasties. When I learned that, through the magic of Too Good to Go, I could get a fresh, tasty pie and two sausage rolls for four pounds, I started going to Waverley station at least twice a week. It would be two more months before I actually caught a train at Waverley, and I definitely enjoyed it less than collecting meat pies.

I had just sat down and taken out my newly acquired pie. I had been too preoccupied with getting my confirmation code out to see which mystery pie they had decided to give me. This fact was not cleared up when I eagerly sank my teeth into the flaky, buttery crust, as I got too distracted by burning the roof of my mouth to taste anything.

As I made little whimpering noises and rapidly blew the pain away, a few fluffy blobs of gray suddenly appeared by my feet. My burned mouth turned up at the corners. Some pigeons had come to make a feast of my fallen pasty crumbs. The poor birds looked like they needed it, too. They were so scrawny, and as more arrived, it was clear that most of them were missing toes and feet. As a native New Yorker, born and raised in Manhattan, I was, of course, used to seeing feral pigeons, both healthy and injured. These little guys, though, were sadder-looking than even the rattiest birds I had ever seen back home.

In New York, the occasional one-legged pigeon was a sad fact of life, but they were still uncommon and could put on enough weight to fend off the coming winter. In the UK, birds missing legs and toes were the majority and always a feather's width away from starvation. Whether it was Edinburgh, Manchester, or London, the hurt and hungry pigeons always outnumbered the few thriving ones. I could guess why New York's pigeons were more well-fed—more people means more trash, and more trash means more scavenging—but it baffled me how the UK's pigeons could so easily suffer. How could people who lived in Edinburgh say my home city was hard to survive in when in theirs, such simple creatures are allowed to perish?

I stopped in the middle of tearing off some of my pasty's outer crust. I remembered the sign that was hanging in the waiting room: DO NOT FEED THE BIRDS. As much as I wanted to feed these poor creatures, I didn't want to be told off for blatantly breaking the rules. I wasn't even afraid of a station employee catching me; for some reason, the thought of a random Scottish person judging me for being ignorant of the rules filled me with more personal anxiety. Back in New York, I was never bothered by the hordes of people who witnessed me living my life and being eccentric. I knew that none of them cared, and if they did, they wouldn't bother saying anything to my face. In Edinburgh, I was once mocked for using a too-ratty umbrella in the middle of a storm. I didn't need any more judgement in my life, much less from someone who was going to yell at me in a Scots brogue for being a no-good out-of-towner.

It was in the midst of this crisis when I saw him. He was sitting on the next bench over to my right; the seats between us were miraculously vacant despite the crowded atmosphere, giving us the space in which to lock eyes.

Typically, strangers look very dull to me. For me to take notice of any random person whom I don't already know, they have to look or act very odd indeed, especially if they're dressed in "normal" clothing, i.e., not cosplay or any disturbing stages of undress.

This person was, indeed, wearing enough clothing to not raise any eyebrows, and each part of his outfit was, more or less, average: grey hoodie, darker grey sweatpants, one tattered right pink sneaker. (His left pant leg ended in a curled metal prosthetic foot. Some people have said I could have added this detail to his list of "unusual features," but I know too many amputees to do that.) What actually stood out about his clothing was the level of grime on it. His clothes were all so worn and smudged with dirt that I couldn't help but wonder if he was homeless. He had added to the grime by tearing into a sausage roll, half of which he clutched in his right hand. Most of the other half coated his shirt and shoe.

No, what really stood out about him were his eyes: his irises glowed a bright, fierce orange. He was already a stern-looking fellow, but those eyes made his glare feel deadly.

As I helplessly stared back at this filthy stranger, his eyes flickered from me to the pasty to the birds gathering beneath me. Then, locking eyes with me once more, he leaned over and shoved the rest of the sausage roll into his mouth. He did this in such a way that crumbs exploded from the thing, coating the ground and the feathers of his own flock of pigeons underneath him. The crumbs were swiftly set upon by his birds, their black and grey feathers easily blending in with the filthy grey of the man's sweatpants.

It took me a few moments, but I finally realised something: He was waiting for me to make a choice.

After blowing on the molten insides of my pasty, I took my own messy bite. The pigeons by my feet fluttered happily as they were showered in pasty crumbs. To anyone watching, I wasn't "feeding" the birds. I was merely eating very messily, letting fate decide what would happen to the crumbs I dropped in the process. Perhaps some people who happened to glance my way judged me for this mentally, but at least no one had a reason to angrily tell me I was breaking the rules.

The man nodded, pleased that I had chosen correctly. Suddenly, his face fell, and he checked a band on his wrist. He must have been checking a watch, but even from a distance, a part of me felt, instinctively, that it wasn't like any watch I had ever seen before.

The man stood up and walked through the crowds of pigeons, who barely reacted to his presence, even with his metal foot. I had stopped watching him by this point, enforcing the New Yorker's unspoken rule of letting strangers (who weren't being assholes) live their own damn lives. While I could see him in my peripheral vision, my eyes were cast down at the birds and at my pie. As he passed me, and I watched a shining metal foot step past my own, he muttered something softly, yet clearly.

"You're far from the city, ain't you?"

I stopped chewing. My breath caught in my throat.
I knew that accent.

I turned to try and see him again, but somehow, in those few seconds, he had vanished. I looked left and right, but everyone around me was an average, non-amber-eyed stranger.

Then I looked down at the pigeons. One of them—one that I didn't remember being among my pigeons before—took off and flew towards the station's exit. As it flew out of sight, I could have sworn that one of its wings had a band around it, and that its left leg ended in something curved and metal.

Kahaniwala

Rasika Bhale

The business of being a storyteller was not an easy one. He worked all night to come up with stories and because he had not yet learned to write, he memorised them laboriously. Out he went in the morning, to villages near and far yelling, "Kahaniwalaaahhh...."

Sighting this middle-aged man, the children rushed to him. They circled him and pleaded with him to tell them a story. But like everything else in the world, even stories didn't come free. He charged three paise for a short story, six for a long one, and ten for a true story. It hardly mattered to his listeners whether the stories were true or not. It fascinated them that what they heard could have happened to someone somewhere else.

Though the children never had any money, the storyteller accepted a handful of peanuts and some chunks of jaggery as payment. They all sat on the ground and gave him a charpoy to sit on. Giggling and whispering, the children were excited, for those were the days when a storyteller was the only entertainment.

As nourishing as the peanuts and jaggery were for his body, what satisfied him most was their enthusiasm to listen. He could see it in their eyes: they were hungry for his stories, and he thought it his noble responsibility to satiate their hunger.

Oh, what stories he told! Women carrying pots of water stopped amidst the scorching heat to hear of the circus clown who couldn't speak. Men were late to their work in the fields, sparing a moment to hear about the woodcutter who felled a tree that wasn't supposed to be felled. People of all ages were drawn to him and his alchemy with words.

He journeyed across villages and towns on foot and found some path to be more pleasurable than the others and some to be more challenging. The winds of time whirled by him without a touch and tongues began to wag about how the old storyteller never seemed to age.

"How old are you?" a child asked him once.

"As old as your father." He replied. He never gave them a number. A grey-haired woman had inquired about his secret to youth, but he smiled, showing his crooked teeth, and assured her that she already looked beautiful: more beautiful than youth would ever make her look.

Years flew by, and the world came to be as we know it today. On his travels, he saw the high-rise buildings and vehicles that covered in minutes the distances he covered on foot in a day. He saw people rushing here, there, and everywhere, but never reaching anywhere. He also saw the children who used to be hungry for his stories. He saw them, their necks bent like those of flamingos, constantly immersed in devices just a little bigger than their hands.

The storyteller worked hard, telling stories about the queen who jumped in the fire or about the parrot who saved an army from being slain in battle, but he could not keep up. It had become a world that wanted to know more but not feel more. He wondered how one could know without having felt, but he, like several others, had become a thing of the past.

Soon the inevitable happened. With no one to lend a listening ear, the storyteller bottled up his stories inside his head and they started leaving him. The marks of time began to show, and the mystery of his youth remained a mystery no more. With eachstory's departure, he grew as old as the woman who had once asked him for the secret to youth. He wondered—what happened to the circus clown or the woodcutter or the girl who read a thousand books? But the truth was that they had all gone away. His characters were alien now, like people he'd encountered in a past life. Dejected, he decided it was time to leave Earth.

He travelled to a galaxy far away, where he found new audiences who were far more attentive than the Earthians. He told them of his business of stories, and they told him they had never heard anything like it. He told them of his queen who jumped in the fire to save herself and of the parrot who carried a letter across a thousand miles that ultimately avoided a war. His stories left them awe-stricken with amusement and wonder, and they produced a loud noise that imitated the clapping of Earthians.

"Do you even understand my language?" he asked them once the applause had died down. They nodded and repeated his story to him in his language. How wonderful it was that language was not a barrier but a medium, he thought. There, he relearned his craft and regained his youth. The Mishandleaurs reveled in his stories and begged him for more. They were unlike humans in so many ways. They always had time to listen. They were beings who were fed data eight hours a day, hence they understood the value of a good story.

"More! More!" they bellowed, their thirst for stories never seeming to be satiated. He lovingly obliged at first, but soon fell short of their demands. They were data beings and nothing seemed to meet their greed.

After some years, the stories stopped coming. He would open his mouth and let out emptiness, unsure of what to do. The Mishandleaurs would stare at him and wait. He would stare back. They were all the same, not one different from the other. They worked the same jobs and ate the same food and slept at the same time and spoke about the same things. He sought in them his circus clown, the woodcutter, and the girl with the ability to fly, but all he found was the boring monotony with which they lived their lives. Soon, he felt a longing: a longing for Earth. A longing for home. How long could he wander in a foreign land, he asked himself. Homesick, he decided to return.

The Earthians, bereft of his stories for all these years, welcomed him with grandeur and joy. The young, the old, the rich, and the poor all crowded around him to hear of his adventures in the far-away galaxy.

"Another story!!" The children cheered.

"About the woodcutter or the talking parrot?"

"No, about the Kahaniwala!" they insisted. The storyteller smiled and looked up at the sky. The shimmering stars made him think of his Mishandleaurs and their land.

"Let's keep that for tomorrow. Right now, how about a young boy who learned to fly?"

"Yay!"

The children yelled with joy, hugged him, and then sat down on the ground again. He ate some peanuts and chunks of jaggery that were spread out on a napkin and began his tale.

"Once upon a time…."

***

My Best Birthday

Claire Wallace

Mama took me to a graveyard for my seventh birthday. It was a fancy graveyard, filled with stone tablets with carved flowers on top and statues of angels looking down at us. Mama apologized when we arrived at the tall metal gate. She said she'd messed up, that she'd find a proper park to take me to. I had asked to go somewhere green for my birthday since the only thing green around us was the garden box that Mrs. Kim watered every day. No one else bothered growing things in the building we lived in, so I would look forward to that box growing green on my way to school. Mama knew I loved that little box, so when I asked, she looked at the map of our gray cement city and found the biggest green space there was. The only thing is she didn't realize that there was a "cemetery" after "Gateway Park." It was green, alright, and I told her as much, but she kept on apologizing. But Mama doesn't need to apologize. Mama says she made too many mistakes, and that's why I gotta live somewhere else for a little bit. But I know that it's all going to be okay. Mama makes things okay.

She makes things okay. Like the pink backpack I took to the graveyard on my birthday. I used my last one so much that the bottom disappeared, so she took me to the shop. It was filled with clothes, shoes, and bags that other people didn't want, but we did. I saw this pink backpack there. I stopped and picked it up, but the number on the tag was too high. I put it down when she asked me if I wanted it. I couldn't lie. It was a bright pink backpack that had princesses on it, like the backpacks some girls in my class have. I told her yes, but it's okay, I'll find another bag I like. The next thing I knew she was hugging the backpack close and taking my hand as we walked towards the exit of the store. I was running along to keep up. Her sweaty hand made it hard to hold on. I just clung tighter. When we reached the sidewalk, we both were running. I laughed and ran as fast as I could. I had Mama and a brand-new pink princess backpack that she'd got for me. I'd never had anything so expensive. I took it everywhere with me, to school, to the library, and to the graveyard on my birthday. I brought it here too, because Mama told me to pack a bag and said she'd be back soon. I don't like it here 'cause they say Mama isn't coming back. But I know Mama is coming. I trust her.

I trust her more than I trust anyone else. We were walking along the path of the graveyard that she took me to for my birthday. I was looking at the flowers people had brought for the people buried underneath. From people who cared about them, Mama told me. I asked her what would happen if you died all alone. There would be no one to put flowers on your grave then. She smiled and said fairies would. I'm old enough to know that fairies aren't real, like Santa. Hard to believe in a Santa that picks and chooses which kids to give presents to. I know 'cause I was on my best behavior for a full year and got nothing from him. I did get a small present wrapped in the comic section of the newspaper. *From Santa* was on the front but I knew it was from Mama. Maybe if I had more presents, I wouldn't have minded thinking Santa got me one. Since there was just one present, I wanted it coming from Mama, not a guy I didn't know. So that's how I knew that when she said fairies. She wanted me to believe in them, but I knew those graves wouldn't get any flowers. I told her I understood. I don't believe in fairies, but I believe in her. I believe that she won't wait long to come get me, no matter what they say.

I believed her when she said she would always take care of me. When we were at the graveyard that we went to for my birthday, she packed a picnic for us. I found an empty bench, without trash or empty cigarette butts, under a tree looking over the spring green grass and the mossy headstones. Mama looked at it and said we should find a place with a better view. But I thought it was perfect, and sat down to enjoy my PB&J. I'd been looking forward to eating a PB&J the entire day. She'd woken up early that morning to make it before we had to catch the two buses to get there. I usually ate lunch at school, and they never had PB&Js or any other food they thought was too sweet. At home we have plain peanut butter sandwiches all the time. I know how to spread a thin layer on half a slice and fold it like a taco when I make lunch on weekends. The jelly is special. Mama keeps a jar of it high in the cabinets only for special occasions. Holidays she puts it on Ritz crackers. When something really bad happens, like when we heard about Mr. Hill's accident downtown, she lets me have a spoonful, and on birthdays she makes a PB&J with two big slices of bread.

I bit into the white bread and the sweet flavor of strawberry spread across my tongue. A glob of jelly almost fell on my dress, but I caught it and stuck my finger in my mouth. Mama didn't yell at me like other adults would. She just handed me a napkin. I offered her a bite because she didn't make one for herself. She said she wasn't hungry and didn't need lunch or breakfast sometimes. I still asked if she wanted a bite, 'cause sharing is caring, and I care about Mama. She told me it was okay, and it was my special treat. She wanted me to have the entire thing 'cause she cares about me. I don't need fancy meals with snacks in between or the perfect cake. I just need Mama and Mama needs me.

Mama needs me. That's what she told me every day. Before we left the graveyard that Mama took me to for my birthday, she told me she was sorry that I didn't have a perfect birthday. I told her it was more than perfect. She told me she loved me, and she was sorry. I told her I loved her too, but I didn't know what she was sorry about, so I just held her hand telling her it was okay. Maybe she was just sad that day. She is sad sometimes, but she doesn't like it when I'm sad. She says she'll do anything to make me happy. I know she'll be back, cause without Mama I won't be happy. And I am happy with Mama. The other kids here that don't have Mamas like mine, they aren't happy. But I have a Mama, so I'm not sad. I still have a Mama. No matter what anyone says, she's coming for me. She promised me.

She did promise me. She promised me the night that we got back from the graveyard that she took me to for my birthday. She asked if I would be happier with another family. I set her straight, that she was my only family. She got sad again. I asked her if she was going to leave. She promised me that she would always be with me.

I want Mama with me now. Okay? And don't take me back to that graveyard that Mama took me to for my birthday. Don't tell me I need to bring flowers for her grave. I'm not going to go, 'cause I know that Mama is still here. I still remember her voice, her hugs, every promise she ever made. I hate when people say Mama is in a better place or in the angels' arms, 'cause Mama isn't dead! She can't be. She made a promise to me.

And Mama keeps her word.

Sebastian

Jason Philip Perlman

With glowing smiles and book-filled backpacks, the children raced into the orphanage's library as if darting through a finish-line. Their voices filled the otherwise quiet chamber where Gramps sat silently and flipped through the worn pages of his favorite book, *Myths and Gods*. He peeled his eyes from the paper and bobbed his head while eyeing each child, mirroring their smiles.

"Gramps! Gramps!"

"You promised!"

"We want to hear the rest of the story!"

"Come on, come on!"

"Hi Gramps, how are you feeling today?" Little Nellie tugged at his pant leg and looked up with the sweetest of eyes: one a vibrant hazel and the other a dulled blue. They reminded him of someone he once knew but could no longer remember.

"Fantastical." Gramps patted Nellie's head and closed the book, allowing his eyes to linger on the cover. He pushed the text a hand's length from the table's edge, positive that no-one would disturb it. Just as he'd watched them grow, they'd watched him reminisce through the same pages day after day.

"Let's move to the green room. You'll have to remind me where I left off." Gramps reached for his cane, a work of art crafted from a yew sapling with several woodland creatures carved into its solid spine: nymphs, fairies, and others whose names had been lost. With a low groan he stood, leaning heavily onto the wood for support. His darned legs had been failing him lately, or had it been a while?

The children ran ahead giggling, all except for Nellie who walked slowly by his side.

He thought about the day he found her crying on the front steps, three or maybe five years earlier. He sat on the steps with her tiny fingers wrapped around his pinky until Mary returned. She'd scolded him for sitting in the rain, but what else was he to do? No child should be left on their own.

The memory carried him to the library's door: a heavy mahogany slab with a dark swirl in its center. Gramps reached for the button, but Nellie beat him to it, pressing both her palms against the silver switch. Magically, the door slid sideways, and Gramps watched with a grin. The two walked slowly, but Gramps's breath hastened.

Cane, foot. Foot, cane.

"How was class today?"

"It was fun! We learned about the weather! An Eclectric Storm is coming."

"Electric—" Gramps nodded at the darkening sky through the room's only window.

"Yeah! Ms. Murphy said it's the biggest one ever!"

"Electrifying!" Gramps joked.

Nellie nodded. "Also! Big sister Louise is coming back. She's bringing her boyyyyfriend."

"Louise," Gramps mumbled under his breath. "Louise, I can't seem to place her."

"She said she wanted to see you and that he has to ask for your approval."

"Louise!" Gramps exclaimed. "Eat your peas, Louise. Louise! Don't chase the cats. Off to sit in the rain Louise? I'll get my coat."

Cane, foot. Foot, cane.

"Gramps! Gramps!" one child shouted as Gramps plodded into the green room.

"Hurry up!"

The children sat gathered around the purple rocking chair, his chair, reserved for him: the lead bard and storyteller. They waited patiently, as patiently as they could for his slow old bones.

Cane, foot. Foot, cane.

He turned and slid into the chair and laid his cane across his lap, smiling at the suddenly quiet faces that looked at him with wonder. "So, what are we talking about today?"

"The story!"

"The goddess!"

"The golden chamber!"

"Gaia was about to meet the Dragon King!"

Gramps nodded and muttered, "Gaia," followed by some incomprehensible tongue. "Is everyone comfortable?"

The children nodded; some pressed their hands into the floor and pushed their bodies closer.

With closed eyes, he recalled the tale: "Gaia strutted into the audience chamber with Sebastian close behind. The chamber was monstrous; it was made for dragons after all. Its walls and floors were built from solid gold with intricate claw-carved patterns etched through their surface, designed by the most famous dragon artist—"

Gramps paused.

"Hyuler," a woman called out.

Gramps steered his sight to a familiar face and squinted. He scanned from eyes to nose to mouth to chin. Had they met before?

"Hyuler!" the children echoed, pulling his attention back to the story.

"Ah yes, Hyuler, how could I forget! He was a wonderful dragon. Had the most beautiful scales. It was as if he'd carved them himself. He painted a portrait of my goddess once—said she was a muse with heterochromia—"

"Gramps!" a child interrupted.

"Rambling, rambling, yes I know. So, Gaia stepped onwards. The King watched us—I mean, them—the entire time, silently waiting." Gramps looked over the children and then to the woman again. "Louise!" he exclaimed, smiling as his eyes locked with hers.

Louise smiled back. "Heya, Gramps."

"Gramps!" a child shouted.

"Gaia strode up to the King. Thraknel was his name. She bowed and I—no, Sebastian followed. It was a long bow, especially for a goddess, one who typically bows to no-one. But for the sake of her people, she lowered her head."

Gramps cleared his throat and leaned forwards in his chair to imitate Thraknel's booming voice, trying to capture the power and confidence that sent shivers down even a seasoned warrior's spine. "*Your soul shines brighter than even I expected. It's as if a dragon sleeps within you. And you, your devotion to your goddess is worthy of a shadow.*" A tear trickled from Gramps's eye.

He continued the tale emphatically until Mary interrupted,

shepherding the protesting children off for dinner and homework. With huffs and sighs, they obeyed; she was the orphanage's director after all.

"Gramps." Mary approached after the children left. "Louise has someone she'd love for you to meet. He is Bertha's grandson. You remember Bertha, right?"

"Bertha—Bertha."

"Bertha the biter," Mary reminded him.

Gramps smiled. "The biter! Gnawed on every piece of furniture just like a teething pup! Tried to take my finger off once or twice! How is Bertha? I haven't seen her in—many years now."

The man stepped forwards and knelt in front of Gramps, clasping his warm hands around Gramps's wrinkled ones. "Gram-Gram is doing good. She just turned ninety-nine a few weeks ago! She talks about you every day. We—I never believed the stories until I met Louise. You really do look just as she described."

"Ninety-nine. That's a fine age. Her ninth birthday was a hoot. She bit right through the candle, wick and all."

As Gramps leaned back in his chair, the eerie howl of the shelter siren pierced through the building and grew into a steady, blaring blast.

Mary's face dropped. "Quickly! Louise, follow me. Jerry, the shelter is in the basement. The staircase. Help Gramps!" She turned and ran.

"I need to help—" Louise started.

"I'll get him there, I promise."

"Ah, another beautiful storm—" Gramps mumbled as the hairs on his neck stood erect. "Gaia. I promise."

"Come on Gramps! We need to move."

Gramps nodded and extended his cane to the floor, standing with Jerry's help.

Cane, foot. Foot, cane.

"Ouch!" Jerry yelped. "Are you okay? Something shocked me!"

Gramps didn't respond, his gait halted, he gazed through the walls. "I feel her." His words slurred. "I will raise them well, guide them."

"Gramps? Who? We have to go! It's not safe here."

"I feel her, but it's different."

"Gramps!"

"No. No. No! I am Sebastian. I can feel her. I'm her shadow."

Louise scurried across the hallway, guiding thirty or so kids into the stairwell: some carrying plates of food, others with books and blankets and colorful stuffed animals in their arms.

Cane, foot. Foot, cane.

"Ouch!" Jerry shouted again as Gramps passed the stairs.

"Carefully now!" Mary called out, overseeing as several of the older children and staff cradled crying babies down the steps.

"I'm coming. I will raise them well."

Cane, foot. Foot, cane.

Gramps pushed open the front door and hobbled outside.

Cane, foot. Foot, foot. Foot, cane.

"Fuck!" Jerry shouted. "Mary! He won't listen! I can't touch him. He's going outside!"

Cane, foot. Foot, foot. Foot, foot. Clank—the cane dropped to the ground.

"Gaia, I promise."

The wind shrieked around him; dark clouds obscured the sky.

"Gramps!" Jerry shouted, unable to pass through the violent wall of wind.

"No." Mary pulled Jerry into the house. "It's finally his time."

Thunder rumbled.

Purple lightning struck.

Gramps turned. His eyes erupted with life—orbs filled with a bright violet glow. He smiled, waved, and vanished into the storm.

The Turn

Alison Schultz

When the moon finally sets, I'm shivering, drenched in sweat. I dig my head out from under my pillow and peel myself off my duvet to close the window, but I'm shaking too much, the lever is too stiff, and my fingers are too clammy. I give up, pressing my hands into the windowsill so hard that my palms ache. I dig my nails into the grooves I left last month, the month before, the month before.

The street is silent under a snowfall that dusts the sidewalk and clings to the spindly ends of winter-dead branches that scratch at me from the other side of the glass. I curl sideways under my blankets, where the heat quickly becomes incendiary. Bile pricks at my throat. If I push my head out, the reek of last night's steak cuts, left to spoil on the hob three rooms over, will sicken me. But if I don't, I'll choke.

I have to get rid of the meat. I pull a sweatshirt over my nose and hold my breath in the kitchen. The casserole dish goes in the bin. The knife goes in the bin. The meat slicks against the side of the bag, dripping into the mess below. I shouldn't have tried to cook it. I couldn't eat at all yesterday, but by the time I turned, I would have devoured it in any form. It seemed like one nice thing to do for myself, despite it all.

I drag the bag out to the street. When I open the lid, the fetor of rotting produce and curdled cashew milk masks the reek of the meat. But when my waste tumbles into it, the stench curls towards my nose, mephitic enough for my stomach to twist violently. I take three steps toward the front door and vomit into the bushes.

In my flat, I swirl mouthwash around my gums, scrub my hands until they're raw, then drench the oven with a sharp-smelling cleaner. I hold the kitchen window open with an empty vegenaise jar and spray the room until the air is clouded with antiseptic.

When I'm done, my shoulders collapse. Soreness stretches along my back where muscles bloomed and then decayed in the space of one night. I throw back four painkillers with a mouthful of water and tumble into bed, trusting that my exhaustion will outweigh the heat of resentment that kept me awake through the dark hours of the night.

Some people say their turn is like a blackout—when the sun comes up, they're sore and stiff but oblivious.

Not mine. I feel it all.

☾

They're eighty-one minutes in by the time I get there, shaking the snow out of my hair.

"Sorry I couldn't get a table," Jay says. I wave him off. I have no right to complain when I slept through the afternoon and the entire first half of the match. I stuff my bag at my feet and scan the pub.

Nearly every face appears normal, natural. There's one girl at the bar whose nose is slightly too pointed. When she turns from the counter, her eyes meet mine, dark and perceptive. I look away, warming with shame.

I don't drink. Drinking after the turn is just as bad as drinking during it. I found both of those out the hard way. Jay insists on getting me something, though, so I ask for water with a sheepish smile. Cold bursts of air alert me to each new arrival, whose features I search, seeking out familiarity. So far it's only me, and maybe the girl from the bar, although she's long since vanished to her table. When Jay returns, I take a long drink from my glass, setting my eyes on the screen above us.

No score, still, but no trouble, either. Our women, defying expectations, have kept their heads down in the run up to the finals. Although the real question was always about today: how they might play, if they'd retaliate. There was a petition a few months back to move the final to a different date than the day after the full moon. The commissioner denied it. Tori Chaussee made the point in her last few interviews that it is absolutely discriminatory to refuse to shift the match, but she's done nothing since to put a target on herself, or her five other teammates who have the same condition that she does, that I do.

You're not supposed to say "condition." It can't be cured. It can't be afflicted. But it feels like one, so I call it whatever I want.

I tell myself it's better that she's made it this far without being carded. If she makes any sort of violent play in response to all the fouls she's received from her opponents, it will end up on every news channel in the world—and I don't need another excuse for people to think I'm a savage. But for her not to have at least tried to make a statement—well, who am I to talk? The whole world knows about Tori's lycanthropy. As much as people may suspect it of me, Jay's the only one who has proof. I avoid anyone else who might understand.

I don't need understanding. I need it out of me.

"You want anything to eat?" Jay asks, noticing my expression.

"No. Thanks."

"Have you had anything since last night?"

"I can't," I say. "Can't eat, I mean. I just…"

"I know. But I want you to feel better."

She's back by the counter, that girl I saw earlier. Jay notices her too.

"You think she's—"

"No," I say. There are so few of us, even here, where allegedly nobody really cares one way or another. But she makes eye contact with me again, and when she comes over, I realize I'm wrong—her features are undeniably wolfish. Dark eyes, sharp face, her nose little too pointed to be natural. My heart skips a beat, but my mouth tastes dusty and raw.

"You guys doing okay?" she asks.

"Sure," Jay says, keeping his expression even. "Why?"

"I don't know. Long night."

There are shadows under her eyes, clouded by concealer. I didn't even try to cover mine. I'm both impressed and resentful that she had the energy.

"Sorry," she says, when neither of us respond. "Didn't mean to assume."

"No, it's—you're right," Jay says. My stomach sinks. "We're—I mean, I managed okay. It's always going to be better than the first, right?"

She smiles, letting her teeth show. "Can't be worse, can it? Now I don't have to completely lock myself up. Still sucks, but my flatmates and I manage. Last night, we watched Star Wars for like nine hours. Made kebabs and shit. Delicious."

I lock my eyes on the screen, but my vision is going soft, fading at the edges.

"You're way better prepared than I am," Jay remarks. "I just dozed for most of it."

"Good on you for trying to sleep. You guys stay together for it?"

Nausea rips through my body. I take a step back, but there are more bodies behind me, trapping me in place. I'm forced to stand my ground.

Jay looks at me, deciding whether or not to lie. It would be so easy, so natural, for me to speak up: *Oh, no, I just look this way. Yeah, unlucky. At least I don't have to deal with all of that. I agree, it must be so hard.* The tension hangs between us.

Then the group behind us groans loudly. Onscreen, Tori pushes onto her elbows. Another dirty blow. There's no penalty. Suddenly she yells out, her face contorted in pain far beyond what the hit called for. She crawls to her feet, then buckles over, her hands pressed into her knees, just as mine were this morning against the windowsill. She screams again, and in it is the sound of all the pain I've been holding onto. The fear, the fury, the hatred, external and internal, driven towards and from within me. My nails cut into my palms as I tighten my fists.

Then she straightens. She shakes off the trainers who have come to her side. She pushes her hair back, takes a long breath, and sprints towards her team.

No penalty. But no card, either.

When the girl looks back at me, there are tears in my eyes.

"No," I say, as the chatter starts up again inside the pub. My blood freezes in my arms, but I take a breath. "I spent the turn alone."

Eggs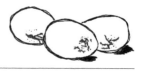

Zain Rishi

Abba does this thing where he takes the bird around the garden, showing her everything she hasn't already seen. Here is the worm under the rock. Here is the garden beyond the fence. Here is the felled tree. In the space between his palms, she twitches, she stares. Her brown feathers are sticky with pollen and dandelion seeds. Her eyes could be human.

On mornings like this, I don't wave or call to him. I look down at their shapes on the rectangle of grass that juts out against the empty pond. Most days, it's normal to see him sat on his camping chair, holding the bird and singing Cat Stevens songs while she pecks at the hard skin around his knees.

In the kitchen, Amma makes me eggs. I come downstairs to the smell of bubbling ghee and spring onions. I hear the chop of the knife against the stems of dhania, the scrape off the wooden board into the pan, how they raise the sizzling by no more than a whisper.

I walk in, cling to her waist, and wonder how long we've been like this. Her shawl has a bitter smell from years of oudh layered into the cloth. Her hair is black and webby and comes down to my eyes. She lets go of the pan and kisses my head.

My baby, my baby, shhh, she says, even though I'm saying nothing.

We stand there for too long, and she only lets go because the eggs are beginning to smoke. She gets flustered, scraping away at the metal until the mass stops holding on, and she flings it into the bin and shoves an empty cereal box on top.

She begins again.

WWW

When Amma leaves for work, Abba is already gone. There is no pattern to when he disappears, only that it is for hours, and he will always bring something home:

Rubber bands.

Tinfoil.

Empty water bottles.

Plain paper.

I look at the pile on the kitchen table, trying to connect it to what I remember of his affection. It sits there, unmoved, purposeful yet unattended. The corner of the stack of paper is wrinkled with yellow fat, crumpled and tacked against the plastic tablecloth.

I go outside to look at the bird while she is sleeping. The last columns of sunlight are landing on the back of the house. The shadows of leaves are stirring and breaking them apart into a patchwork with the wind.

Her breathing thrums against the gaps in the metal netting. One day, Abba removed the base of her cage and jammed the sides into the earth, but I remember the sound when the floor was still there. The sharps of her feet searching for soft earth, finding nothing but more of the metal she could already see in every direction.

She's the size of a small cat now. I imagine her tiny heart beating beneath the layers of feathers. She seems so peaceful, and I try to reach in so that I can touch her for a moment, just like Abba does.

But she stirs.

She shoots up onto her feet, flapping and screaming at me. I fall back and scramble against the ground, kicking away chunks of moss. When I get back up, my clothes are green and muddy. I look up and see Abba blinking at me across the empty pond. I say nothing. I walk back inside and run upstairs and bury myself in a blanket. I wait for Amma to come home.

/\/\/\

Soft-boiled. Jammy yolks and flecks of uncooked white.

She taps the teaspoon against the shell, making fractures in the tiniest universe. The shards come down, and with her hand over mine we scrape out the inside, scooping out every last bit as she tells me I'm getting big and strong.

I hear him out there in the dark. I hear him hack at the bush with all his might, panting as he strips it naked of all its leaves.

I think of the bird, shivering in her cage.

I think of Amma, staring out the window as she raises the spoon to my orange lips.

In the morning, the house is empty apart from me. Amma is working. Abba is out. I tell myself I will not go outside again. The bush has been ripped to pieces. It looks like fragments of something that never had an original shape, parts of a sentence that said nothing at all.

Next to the pond, I can see a mound of dirt that I never noticed before. I watch the bird as she nestles in the corner of her cage. I tell myself I will not go outside again, but I head downstairs and open the garden door.

The grass is itchy against my bare ankles and feet as I walk over to the mound in Amma's slippers. As I get closer, I can see it dips in the middle, like whatever's inside has sunken in and shifted.

I claw away the dirt with both hands. I take chunks and throw them behind me. I keep going. I start to fling them away to the sides, at the fences, at the air above my head. It's only when I take hold of the crackly mush in my hand—the first egg—that I bring myself to stop.

In the ground, there are about fifty of them. The ones at the top are fresh, unbroken. But deeper into the pile they are like swollen boils. Purple, brown, black. They bleed into each other, marbling with the underlayer of wet dirt. The air stinks of sulphur.

I look over at the bird and wonder if she knows this is where Abba put her children, whether she can hear the ground below babbling, chirping, the chicks breaking out in a language that never meets the worldly air.

I think of all the restless nights when he tears everything down, the slam of the tree, the beating of her wings as she cries in the dark.

In the morning, he'll hold her, brush her wings and sing to her before he vanishes and comes back—only to do it all over again.

I think of Amma in a bigger cage.

I go back inside to get Amma's bag. I fill it to the brim with the eggs and carry it to the kitchen and pour them out onto the table.

VV\/\

When Amma comes home and sees what I've done, she starts to weep. I tell her that I did this for us, so we can show Abba what he's done, but she tells me I'm a stupid boy then chokes on her words before I run into the corridor and she catches me and pulls me in and tells me I'm sorry I'm sorry I can't explain and I'm sorry I didn't mean that I'm sorry I'm sorry my baby shhh I'm sorry.

I'm crying with her, my voice filling the silence between her sobs, and we're crumpled in the corridor and my hands are covered in eggs and dying eggs and mud so much mud Amma I miss you even though you're right there why does everything in our life end up this way I'm sorry I'm such a stupid boy I'm sorry I'm—

VV\/\

Poached. Like a raindrop to water I land, and there in the simmer, her heat makes me whole again. Makes us something.

We throw away the rotting eggs from the garden, wipe the table with antiseptic, and clean the dirt around our fingernails an faces.

Her hand over mine, we take out the eggs from the water, the ones she bought from the market, and place them on the cold, white plate. We eat until our stomachs are full but yearning for more.

Abba does not come home today. The men from the mosque call to say he is now living with a friend and painting his fences. Amma cries into me, buries her face in my hair. I cry into her stomach as the sunlight gets taken away.

I walk outside and look at the bird—the hen—shivering as the distant wail of a car horn falls and rises somewhere in the night. I pull the cage out of the ground and set it aside. I wrap her in a blanket, lift her carefully, and carry her inside. We sink into the sofa.

She's so quiet that she almost feels like a question, a space for an answer even though she is right here.

I hold her tight and listen to her sleepy breaths, her gentle coo which hums through the pair of us. I run my hand through the feathers on her back as she tucks her head into her body, her eyes flickering before they come to a still.

The New Spiders

Lily Bastock

I used to have a friend that was afraid of spiders.

Almost everyone has always been a little afraid of spiders. So most people didn't think anything of it when Charlotte said that she was, because they were all a bit scared too. It was hard not to be scared of them. They've always been silk-spinning, meat-liquefying, juice-sucking, many-eyed, many-legged, thick-fanged creatures.

It's nearly impossible not to be frightened now.

Charlotte wasn't just a little afraid. She had arachnophobia—the whole planet's got that now, but at the time we thought it was really funny. I remember how she shrieked when a tiny little thing with eight black legs danced up onto the wall beside her. Tarantula was the 'T-Word'. We couldn't say it; if we did, she would gasp and pull at her hair and brush herself down like she was covered in them. One day we had gone into a Wiccan shop on a whim, just being silly teenagers, and I had laughed maniacally when Charlotte had screamed at the sight of one pinned up in a glass case, splayed out like a pressed flower.

I wasn't laughing when one of the New Spiders bit her, and her eyes rolled back into her head and her skin started to ripple, her cheek sliding down from her eye, blood beading from her pores. She was screaming, screaming worse than she had in the Wiccan shop, until she couldn't anymore because her tongue was like a wet sponge. And then she didn't have a tongue anymore. Everything, all her flesh, was melting off her, and where her arm had been bitten there was nothing left, just bone and bits of bubbling meat and a growing red puddle beneath her that a hundred New Spiders with their blue striped backs were scampering over. They were drinking up what she had become, what she'd been turned into—just a splat on the side of the road. Spilled Ribena.

*

My family and I are driving down the road.

At night, we are never sure whether it's better to have the lights on or off. Lights let them know where we are, but spiders like the dark. It's a gamble. They track with vibrations—at least, old spiders did, we think, and so we assume that the New Spiders track like that too. The world is their web now, and our little black car is a fly trying to escape it.

Dad smiles at me in the rear-view mirror. He lost his false teeth a few months ago, and he's self-conscious of the gaps between his real ones. Whenever he smiles now, he rubs his mouth after, feeling the empty spaces. He frowns, sighs, and thrums his fingers on the steering wheel. The year has aged him. He's fifty. Last year he looked forty, and now he looks sixty. He's thin. The tattoos on his hands are blurry—blurrier for me, because my glasses aren't strong enough anymore, and the lenses are scratched, and Specsavers doesn't exist.

In the passenger seat, mum's chewing the skin off her thumb while she stares out the window. There's a skeleton laid out on the pavement. Because of how they eat you, there's no way for us to know if that person was alive ten months ago or ten minutes ago. Mum has her feet pulled up. She says it's because it's more comfortable, but I think she's scared to let her legs dangle in the darkness under the dashboard. She's even thinner than my dad because she refuses to eat unless she thinks me and Dad have had enough. It's hard to look at her. Sometimes, a nasty voice in my head tells me that she wouldn't take long to liquefy.

There's a woman standing by the side of the road. Her eyes are glassy. I don't think we should stop, but my dad has always been kind. Too kind. My mum told me that she fell in love with my dad because beneath his tattoos and piercings, he has a really good heart. She saw it when he'd stop everything he was doing to help old ladies carry their shopping, and when he would buy cups of tea for the homeless. Back when there were old ladies and homeless people. He liked the way she smiled when she danced. Back when she smiled and danced.

So my dad stops the car. He cuts the engine because of the vibrations. My mum is biting her thumb even harder as he rolls down his window. We are probably quite lucky to still be a family—this woman is probably thinking *what lucky people, having a family and a car.*

"I'm alone," she tells my dad, and I notice she's got really bloodshot eyes. Like maybe she hasn't blinked for a long time. "Can I get in?"

"Open the door, will you?" My dad says.

"Maybe—"

"She's alone," my dad tells my mum. She goes quiet, so I open the door, and the stranger gets in next to me.

My dad restarts the engine, and we begin to drive away. She's got blue eyes, and I can't stop staring at her because she is the first stranger I've met in a month and she's in my family's car and she's sitting next to me. My mum keeps looking at us in the rear-view mirror.

"What are you doing out here?" my dad asks.

"I got lost."

Her voice is smooth like a mirror. She seems very calm. She still hasn't blinked.

"Are you alone out here?"

"No," she answers. She's starting to smile.

She reaches into her coat. She's staring at me. Her smile is wide, and her eyes are as blue as the spider's stripes.

We've made a mistake.

For as long as there has been life there have been weirdos and the old weirdos would keep old spiders as pets and call them Shelob. The new weirdos keep New Spiders as pets and call them God.

Before she pulls out the little jar with a blue and black spider in it I've thrown myself at her and my dad has sworn and my mum has screamed like how Charlotte screamed when she saw the dead tarantula and I've pulled the door handle open and the woman with blue eyes and I are rolling down the road together. Glass shatters. Tires screech. I can hear the woman's laughter, and then her laughter cuts off, and she is shrieking. Pain lances up my arm as though a fang has been driven up the length of it, through palm and wrist and elbow and shoulder and then my entire body is burning and I burn—

*

I'm alive. My parents are standing over me, and the weirdo is dead. The burning is gone, and I feel illuminated. Connected. Soothed to the sound of a thousand whispers that I'm not alone.

I can hear them. They're coming.

"Go," I tell my parents. They hesitate, so I say again, "Leave!"

The final thread to who I was breaks. They look horrified, confused, but I'm happy because I'm not a puddle like Charlotte. I smile. I laugh. My life is unwinding, and I'm spinning a new self.

They're tail lights by the time my friends come. My army. My spiders.

*

I used to be afraid of spiders.

Almost everyone's a little afraid of my beautiful friends. I feel them dance over my skin. Thousands of them brush the hairs on my arms with their hook-nailed toes, hang from my hair by their silky webs, crawl over my lashes with their fuzzy abdomens. They make tunnels in my mouth.

Their blue-striped black backs, and fangs that drip cerulean, glitter like falling diamonds as they dangle from the ceilings of my castle. I can hear their ethereal whispers in the hollows of my mind. Their thoughts cloud my own.

I did not die when the spider bit me, but rose. An aquamarine spider queen on a throne of silk and death.

About Writing

Xiaohui Yue

Whenever you hang your hands above the keyboard in mid-air, ten fingers stretched apart, you feel like you have the whole world at their tips, waiting to be explored and tapped into existence. Stroke after constant stroke, you give life to meaningless letters and give meaning to dry words. You start with sheer passion, pure faith, want to set out on a work and finish it as something that could make a difference, not necessarily a noticeable one for the general public, but even a minor skip of a heartbeat in a single individual would suffice. But almost always you leave behind aborted projects, cancelled plans, revoked promises, convince yourself that nothing matters, not even words. Especially not words.

You lie back, close your eyes, your head against the back of your chair. You sigh and find yourself lost.

That's when you hear the voice.
'Do as I say, and you shall find the way out.'
You look around in panic.
'Who's speaking?'

'I am you as you are me.'

You don't want to believe this. You'd rather believe you are hallucinating. But you know you believe it. You believed it the first time you heard the voice, the voice that's undeniably yours.

'Where are you?'

'That's irrelevant. Just do as I say.'

You pause, think, and relent.

'Fire away, then!' you shout, as loud as you can.

'Go to the southernmost corner of the city and you shall encounter a small hill. Dig into it from the center of the right side until you find a wooden box. It will be the size of your palm. Take it out and open it. Inside the box you will find a sheet of paper lying on golden silk. On it will be written the way out. That is the cure you desire right now.'

You find this most curious and mysterious. But at this stage of your life, you are not occupied with any other undertakings. Your life is a life of writing, and you know you will need a stimulus for your next work before you lose the purpose of living. You decide to listen to your own voice and to seek the box out, even though right now it's three in the morning.

You push open the wooden door and it squeaks in congratulations. Already you know you will find something; already you are pumped full of adrenaline.

The moon is a full disk hanging low and bright under a pink veil. The shrubs on your way are rustling, probably because of the wind, or maybe because of some other things. It will take you an hour to walk there and you pray to bump into no other soul. Who walks in the city this late? It's only madness, you know.

Usually, you go about the city with your cell phone. Google Maps guarantees your way out and your way home. Halfway there, you realize you are alone and ill-equipped. No cell, no flashlight, no digging tool. But already there are so many aborted projects, cancelled plans, revoked promises in your writings, and you don't want them to poison your actual reality. You march on, not sure where you are going, but you don't stop. You seem so sure of where you are heading.

Shortly, you see the hill, the size of a fancy garden gazebo, a mauve silhouette the shape of a ragged pyramid against the cold moon. You shiver out of impatience, out of surprise, out of chill. You only want to rush to business. So you sprint to the hill's right side, measure the distance with outstretched steps. You kneel, pinpoint the central point by placing on the exact spot a yellow tree leaf that smells putrid and is already turning mushy. Nevertheless, you use it. You get up and look around. There's a pointy rock shining silver, resting majestically over a bulging tree root. You snatch it up, kneel again and start digging.

The dirt is loose, sandy, and wedged with tiny stones. You speed up your gouging and soon a much smaller hill forms behind you. You pant and soon become sweaty. Your eyes shine and turn hazy. Your eager hands are soon bleeding. Your nails are grimy. You don't stop. You don't slow. You are in quite a frenzy.

That's when you hear the voice.

'Chill, take a breath, chill. The box isn't going anywhere. What's yours will always be yours and yours only. Take a break and take it easy.'

You can already reach the entirety of your upper body into the hole, and you think there is no reason to take a rest at this point of promising progress.

'Leave me alone, why don't you?' you croak, and decide not to listen to your own overcautious voice that reminds you too much of the days when you were broke, when the money on your table just flapped its wings and flew out of the window, when your clothes and bed sheets ripped themselves into pieces, when even your buddy the

Skinny Ugly Mousey had moved out of your bed-living-dining room.

'You don't want to hurt your fingers, do you? Just look at them, you will be sorry.'

Any mention of your fingers puts you on full alert. You pause midway and notice your hands are shaking. In semi-darkness you see black and red and brown and ivory,\; the colors paint your hands heavenly. You pull them out of the hole, admire them under the shimmering sheen. Thank you, Luna, for turning my craftsman's hands into tonight's first miracle scene. Earth and blood and mud and lime mingle and strew over your skin. You can't register their pain, their twitch, their agony. Instead, you exclaim: What a lovely pair of hands under the moon's illumination!

You are happy, you are possessed, you are almost crying.

To restrain from feeling too over-the-top you slap yourself in the face. There are certain moments when certain feelings need to be strangled. You always seem to know when the moments are and how to enact the execution. How to domesticate your bursting adrenaline, and how to make them work their practical sorcery. Turning them into words is your usual strategy. But tonight, you turn them into the perpetual strength for your digging. Digging for a brighter revelation.

You stoop and turn and re-enter the gaping hole, pick up the silver rock again and scoop out more dirt and more stone.

Bam! There's a dull thud. You know you've just hit the gold. You throw away the rock and carefully peel off the dirt around the protruding wooden corner. You peel and peel and soon it lands on your palm. Indeed, their sizes match perfectly.

That's when you hear the voice.

'Congratulations!'

'I know. I know.' You gasp and moan. The excitement overflows.

You sit, your hip against the inside of the hole in the hill.

You need a moment of absolute peace and quiet. No man, no insect, nobody dead or alive should intrude on your solitary territory.

Next you crawl out of the hole.

The full moon is spilling right over your head. Its light descends in a long, straight path onto the surface of the wooden box you cradle lovingly inside the crook of your right arm.

You kneel and lay the box in front of you, with movements ever so gentle. Your lips tremble. Your tears also.

You wait.

'What are you waiting for?'

'Shut up! This is the moment I need to savour.'

'Suit yourself. You've made it this far. Can't say you don't deserve it after all the toil.'

You sure know it, and you don't bother to reply to your own voice anymore.

Soon, you know you are ready. You press your hands together and utter an invocation.

'Help me, Father, show me the road.'

You flip open the tiny, bolted lock, take out the rolled-up sheet.

Clouds are gathering, shrouding Luna, the sweetest beauty.

With the light of a tenacious moonbeam,

you look onto the paper, and

read out the exact words

you are now

reading.

Threadbare Heart

Raine Bracken

Fate was woven in the pitch black of the place between worlds. An empty void where histories were written long before they took place. Or so it had been, but as lives had been born and lost, their story became inscribed in the stars, etched into the inky blackness. The language of the stars was one few could read, but the Fates knew it well; they had written it.

"Now who do we have here?" asked the Crone, her voice haggard and ancient but firm.

All three of the Fates sat at their looms, their wheels spinning at a divine pace. To mortal eyes they would appear to be floating in a sea of stars. Though they were three they worked as one, spinning a singular tapestry. They sat in a perfect triangle; Mother, Maiden, and Crone, their creation appeared at its centre.

"It looks like a woman." The Mother's voice was gentle, the sort that might urge flowers to grow or lull a weeping child to peace.

"But who will she be?" asked the Maiden, the most curious of the three. There was a glint in her eye as she peered around her loom to catch a better glance of the form taking shape before them: a round face, limbs with a softness that disguised the muscle underneath. They did not weave the flat tapestries of the mortal lands they influenced. Their creations took the shape of that whose life was being written. First a mess of overlapping threads, then the vague form of a body, but as the process drew to an end the details carved themselves onto the figure. Their very fate was woven into their faces, their flesh, their being. It would seem an arduous, time-consuming process to do this with every human being who ever had or would exist, but the Fates existed in a place without time.

"Who is she?" the Crone echoed, as though she were tasting the words on her tongue. "That's the great question, isn't it?"

As their final threads settled into place and their spinning wheels slowed, the Crone held out her palm, and from the ether a simple silver bowl appeared.

"Let's see, shall we?"

Her hand, as gnarled as the roots of an ancient willow, swirled in a circular motion over the rim of the bowl. The Crone drew a single piece of paper. Unfolding it, she held it close to her face. At this point, her milky white eyes could only see out of sheer stubbornness. She raised a single sparse, snow-white brow at the word written there.

"Well?" the Maiden urged.

"Hero."

They were surprised. Not shocked, they were too old for that, but mildly surprised.

"You don't see many of those anymore." The Mother's eyes were filled with pity. "Poor thing."

Heroes rarely had happy endings or easy lives, even in the Age of Heroes when they'd been recognized, worshipped, and necessary. They'd become less common as monsters dwindled and the perils that plagued the world had become more complicated. People didn't want heroes nowadays.

The Maiden clicked her tongue. "What a terrible fate. Especially for a woman." This wasn't because she thought women made poor heroes. There had been a time when the Maiden's eyes were alight with excitement whenever they were able to weave a heroine. She was an embodiment of youth and revolution after all, but the years had taught her that the human world was not as accepting of revolution as she.

"What happened to the last woman hero, again?" asked the Crone.

"They burned her," replied the Mother.

"At least they don't do that much anymore." The Crone dropped the paper and the bowl. Both evaporated into black smoke before they hit the ground.

No, they usually didn't burn them anymore. Not literally, anyway. Still, it seemed as time drew on, humans liked heroes less. They loved them so long as it suited them. They loved them only until they saw a way to tear them down. And how they relished tearing them down. Especially the women.

Humans had a violent sort of hatred for powerful women. The men hated being surpassed by those they considered lesser, but it wasn't just them. Women held a special resentment for any among them that had risen above their expected station. Sometimes they were the quickest to pull them back down and trample on what remained. Their legacies set alight and left to burn, until all that remained were ashes.

The Fates were not those sorts of women, though some might question their character if they were the ones to write these stories. In truth, there was little that could be done. They would have changed things if they could, but they only had so much to work with. They could weave the tapestry, but they couldn't change the wool.

This wool, in particular, was very set in its ways. The Fates had long since lost hope that their creations might change. There were individuals who shone, those who thought, created, and inspired. But as a whole, they were chaos of the worst sort. Now, the Fates just watched with morbid fascination as the stories they'd woven unfolded.

"There is one thing left to determine." The Mother reached into her pile of wool and pulled out two spools of blood red wool, or so they first appeared, but upon closer inspection they were finely woven anatomical hearts. Though woven, they beat in her hands like they'd been torn from a creature's chest. "What sort of heart shall she have?"

She held a heart in either hand as though she were a scale weighing the options and their outcomes.

"I will say I think she'll have an easier time if she were to be hard of heart." The Mother raised one hand higher than the other, answering her own question. This heart did indeed appear hard, its cords woven so tightly together it would take much strength and effort to have it unravel. It was a heart as strong as steel. Unbending but unfeeling.

The Crone smiled. The few teeth she had left shone between the gaps of blackness. "Aren't fragile hearts much more interesting, sister? Humans are so much more interesting when they're breakable. A heart of steel is useful, but pain makes for much better stories." She spoke with infinite wisdom and the sardonic humour of someone with little left to lose.

"I'm not sure if the story is really what we should be focusing on." The Mother's voice was laced with distaste.

"It's all we have to focus on," replied the Crone. "When she's gone, her story will be all that is left of her. It's our job to weave it the best we can."

The Mother looked at her other hand in contempt. In it lay a threadbare heart. One that would fray and feel. It would be harder to withstand the brutality of the world with a heart such as this.

"What do you say?" The Mother turned to the Maiden.

The Maiden looked closely at the hearts, her forehead creasing as she frowned. Those lines would never stay long, for her flesh alone remained like porcelain even after centuries.

"I don't think the best choice for her and the best choice for the story are entirely at odds," she said finally. "Humans are strange. Their pain does not always signify weakness. In fact, sometimes pain is where their strength is born."

The Maiden, being the deciding vote, took the threadbare heart from the Mother's hand. The Mother didn't stop her. At the end of it all, the welfare of one didn't really matter to the Mother. Maybe she would suffer, but what was it to them? As many would say: the Fates are cruel.

The Maiden approached the woven body, still tethered to their looms by its threads. She twisted and ducked to avoid the strands that spread out like a spider's web. When she reached the strung corpse, she pushed the heart into its chest. The strings gave way under her hand, granting her entry as she placed the heart in the cavity. As soon as her hand had lifted, the yarn began snapping back into place, swallowing the red heart whole.

"I can see it now. It's written in the stars," said the Crone. And indeed it was, the path of her life now glittering dots above their heads, a tale spun in silver.

The Crone began cutting loose the threads that still bound the body to their looms.

"It's beautiful," said the Maiden, gazing up at the stars.

"It's terrible," replied the Mother.

"It's written." And with that the Crone cut the last thread.

Terminal

Charlotte Haley

gren_fairy_76: *anyone else think she looks really chubby in her most recent IG post?*

g0rge0usPink: *she always looks horrendous these days. she used to be sooooo much prettier*

Steph wiped a hand over the greasy parting of her hair. Slick, almost wet-feeling. Her phone screen was clouding up with the smudges from her fingers. At least she had finally brushed her teeth—people always said that was the most important thing.

Sun streamed in the living room window, but she was in the shadows. She sighed, nestling into the worn leather of the sofa. You have to go where the warmth is, she thought, and the lounge was the warmest room in her flat during the winter months. Her laptop, discarded, blinked absently at the other end of the sofa, near her feet. Her work used to be important to her, but now the dark screen reflected only her blanketed body and half of her unwashed face.

That morning, she had muted another group chat; its bulbous notification joined the tens of other messages from friends and colleagues that lingered, red and unopened, whenever she went on her phone. Having them there, day after day, was like knowing there were tumours in her lungs but not having access to chemo; like a clump of phlegm she just couldn't cough up. Some things worked as a distraction, though. Things like *Whisperer Online*, a forum that flooded her brain with the usual guilty dopamine as she sought the most recent posts on Twitch streamer, QueenPink, the subject of the only discussion board she ever visited.

F_bot92: *She was even more vapid than normal on stream last night – if that's even possible*

xYellowToadx: *Does anyone else think there might be something seriously wrong with her? She's so slow and ditzy… Idk I'm not a doctor*

clutchtwin: *i didnt think that was possible !*

clutchtwin: *definitely !*

jelly_85_soldier: *Hey guys I've just managed to catch up with this thread - it's going way too quick to keep tabs on*

Stephen_rexx: *Last nite on stream she was so annoying omfg i wanted to tear my eyeballs out – when she miaowed for the chat I wanted to die shes such a 51ut*

jelly_28_soldier: *There are other ways to criticize QueenStink without being rude about her mental state – come on guys this is the stuff that makes this forum seem like it's full of haters, instead of people with legitimate criticism of an online creator* xYellowToadx: *Yeah I agree*

clutchtwin: *totally xx*

Steph continued to scroll through the comments. She'd never contributed in the two months since she'd discovered the site. Although, she had once signed up for an account in a fit of drunken mischief under the username Queen_Bitch_89. Her eyes constantly sought the most damning criticism, the insults that would turn someone's stomach if they heard them out loud. Written in pixels, the vitriol was muted, like the screen was meant to say things real mouths wouldn't dare.

She never even watched Twitch streams—that was one social media platform that seemed to be just outside her generation's grasp—but it seemed QueenPink had the forum up in arms about last night's test play of an unreleased game called *Yes Town*. A handful of commenters were unforgiving of her poor performance with the demo, complaining that she'd purposely shown no skill, or that she'd done the game developers out of money by presenting *Yes Town* as too difficult to be fun. Steph rolled her eyes at these voices. They'd wasted most of their evening watching the four-hour stream only to gripe about it into the early hours of the morning on a forum. Pathetic.

Most contributors to the discourse, though, preferred to insult her make-up, her weight, her especially excessive cleavage, her way of pandering to the perverts in the chat. Those were the comments Steph would seek out, could understand. There was a primal energy in them, an attempt to capture the skull-bashing, cave-painting brutality of the Neanderthal in tearing QueenPink, a twenty-four-year-old streamer from Yorkshire, down to her most vulnerable core. Those tasted of something real.

Steph flicked to QueenPink's Instagram. Staring at the streamer's smooth, young skin and perfect pink wig, the curls cascading down her front, she felt a rush of something lava hot. QueenPink's body contorted in cartoonish low-necked dresses, with pinched-in waists and flared-out skirts that made her seem younger than twenty-four. Her Instagram feed was littered with pictures posed with fans—at the park, at conventions, at the beach.

The couch squeaked as she shifted into a new position. She considered going back to the forum, joining in the most recent discussion on QueenPink's Instagram post from last night and her potential weight gain. Steph's skin prickled at the thought of entering the discourse, of crafting careful comments about QueenPink's appearance, her dilution of feminism, the way she made her eyes wide like a child when gifted subscriptions on Twitch. Steph would write comments that would get a hundred likes: damning indictments of QueenPink's influence over young girls, the threat she posed to women's progress, and the insult to generations of women before her. She'd ruin QueenPink, force her to apologise in viral videos, make her cry on camera and kill her corporate brand deals. It'd be a spiral, a nosedive into obscurity and cancellation. The end of it all. But what if they traced it all back to her? They. Who? She. Warm. Pink.

Steph flicked back to the forum. New comments poured in each minute, dissecting QueenPink's every perceivable online movement, concocting rage when there was nothing posted at all. Her absence of activity that morning seemed to provoke them.

clutchtwin: *where tf is she today???*

g0rge0usPink: *probably out with HotNina22 thinking of the best ways to make themselves look like total wh0res online* jelly_85_soldier: *I have no issue with women expressing their sexuality. I happen to think that Gianna Barnet is an influencer who does it very tastefully. But QueenPink's flagrant pandering to the men in her audience is frankly disgusting. She obviously doesn't value her young fan base, or she just has no morals at all.*

clutchtwin: *loooooool she's such a s1ut!!!!*

KingStink666: *her tits arent even that nice put them away stupid bitch*

xYellowToadx: *can't wait for whatever inane content she'll post today*

Steph's fingers hovered over the text box at the bottom of the screen. She typed.

Queen_Bitch_89: *Hi guys, first-time commenter. I know this has been raised before*

She paused, looking at the sun on the whorls of laminate flooring, breathing the warm smell of morning. Her work email blinked to life on her laptop screen, active since she'd knocked the keyboard while moving onto her side, into the foetal position.

but I just wanted to weigh in. I think QP's blatant disregard for the kids in her audience and the way she sexualises herself is a serious problem that we should report to Twitch moderators. If enough of us agree to report her, I think we could really make a difference. Sorry to get all serious, but I'm just a concerned parent looking for some help.

Steph submitted the comment and waited, anxiety and excitement glittering her chest. She couldn't breathe. The parenthood part had been a bit much but it came out like the truth. She held her breath, letting as many moments elapse as she could bear, then refreshed the page and scrolled down, fingers trembling. A comment was under hers.

> jelly_85_soldier: *I totally agree. She's a threat to modern feminism. Congrats on ur first post! Welcome.*

Split Cream

Salvör Sólnes

She slid the spoon over the soft white surface of the cream. She often thought of its tender sweetness when she crawled into bed at night, snowy peaks in the mixing bowl.

When whipping cream, it must be of a heavy sort and cold, in a clean, dry container. These are also the ideal circumstances for sleep—no mascara tracks on the pillowcase or dry crumbs in the sheets to disturb the task at hand. It's better to leave the window open all day, let the breeze blow through, the air in constant motion. Whip your clothes off in a hurry, pour yourself out of the packaging. Slide, quickly, under the cool duvet. She shivered under the comforter, trying to stir herself gently to sleep. They had always disagreed on this, him preferring to let the room become humid with the scent of human cohabitation.

On his first birthday with her, she made him a pair of lumpy wool socks to keep him warm. Later, she made him a quilt. Fingers advancing from clumsy to practiced, crocheting square after square of itchy wool. On her ring finger was a small lump formed by years of holding a pen; working with the smooth needle formed a twin on her index finger, a blister of devotion. When she presented the enormous blanket to him, her cheeks were hot—a physical display of the mortifying scope of her affection.

Her mother liked to refrigerate the whisk and the bowl before whipping cream, chilling small pieces of her warm kitchen to facilitate her craft. Her mother's whipped cream turned out faultless every time, sweet hills and stiff peaks of white. She wished she could place herself on the cool white shelves to chill her body and mind.

When her father died, her mother stopped cooking. Taken to drinking cans upon cans of cola, glutting herself on the shortages of her childhood. Trying to sip sweetness back into her body.

When they visited her mother together, they would try to feed her carrots and spinach, gleaming cuts of white fish, steaming bowls of lobster soup, spooning all the fragrant meat into her bowl. He had been so kind then, already equipped with skills to draw the women in her family out from the fog of their thoughts. Teasing them into smiling together, breaking the serene stillness of their company. Those nights she would hold him close in bed, breathe in the warmth of him, the sour note of sweat, before retreating to her single, thin duvet, chest brimming with sweetness.

Some nights, when the radiator is too forceful and the duvet too heavy, sleep bubbles over her like viscous honey. Stagnant air oozes into her dreams, which become thick and damp. The delicate peaks of cream start to sweat, churn into butter. On these nights, she awakes with fingers tightly clasped, a clammy grasp around her belly, like his hands had been in the casket. Her shoulders taut, like her body is leaving without her. She needs to breathe deeply and turn the body-warm duvet over, wiggle her toes free of tension. Try to let dreams drift over her, her awareness becoming floaty and feathery.

There are also nights where peace is distant, and her mind

roils with memories. She was hopeless at mountain names—he had always been good about pointing them out from the car window, patiently repeating the stories behind each name every time they drove home. Strange tales of outlaws and wights that tired farmers created to entertain hungry children in the dark. Without him, the umbilical cord to her surroundings was cut, and everything passed her under a veil.

Before, the whir of her thoughts was difficult to still, data from the lab shuffling like a deck of cards across her closed eyelids. Plans for the future kept her awake even in the cool darkness of their room. But a mind buzzing with possibilities is easier to calm.

No possibilities stretch out before them anymore. Only a cheap plot in a graveyard in the next town over. Hours from the snug warmth of the drive home, socked feet on the dashboard, wet smell of shoes in the trunk.

*

These days, she takes the bus to work, lets herself be enveloped by the bustle of other people in the morning, packs a book but ends up staring out the grimy window. The radiator in the bus has been broken for a few weeks, and everywhere chins are huddled in the cradle of scarves to keep warm. Every Thursday, the bus is filled with primary school children, their harried minders shooing them to the back where she sits. The first time, she was startled by the revelation that the teachers were all around fifteen years her junior. She could hear the blurring influence of English in their speech, their grammar and syntax, their drawling lack of clarity. They were around the age she had been when they met in the dingy university bar. Where he had lamented the lack of funding going to language preservation and exclaimed at the warmth of her fingers when he clasped them in his calloused palm.

Yesterday, an old man behind her retched a series of loud coughs. A sound like his lungs were trying to crawl up his throat. His muddy trousers filled the back of the bus with the pungent smell of piss and spilled spirits. She felt a kinship with the hacking man—in another age, she might have handed him her handkerchief. Her mother drank too, she had found out much later. Not for pleasure but methodically—sharp clear spirits gulped down her throat, enabling her to sleep.

Later in the day, she watched two of her coworkers smooth their palms over their swollen bellies and grumble about the lack of back support in the office chairs. Her eyes met with the taller one, who reddened and smiled clumsily at her. Last year, they had talked about going off birth control and the safety precautions that necessitated a break from lab work during pregnancy. They'd giggled together at the prospect of being relegated to office duties. She grimaced back, a facsimile of courtesy, and tried not to focus on the hot stench of dried blood coming from the pad in her underwear.

When she closed her eyes, she prayed not to see that last memory of his face. Like wax poured over his skeleton, cheeks turned to sunken putty retreating from the open air. It had been almost ten days before they could have the funeral, his father flying from Norway, his sister from the East, and his mother from a cheap cruise. She had sat blankly in their room all the while, wishing that they had not laughed at weddings, that their paper trail was not just a series of boxes from his office. His mother had insisted on the open casket.

*

Tonight, the pillowcase is silky and fresh. The veil of sleep creeps up on her while she strokes comfortingly over the gooseflesh of her arms. From her dreams, she awakens softly, her jaw open and vulnerable. The sunrise warms the vaulted ceiling sky, the puckered mouth slackens in a deep exhale. This time of year, morning light creeps softly over the horizon, leaving behind the pitch black of winter; the days where the light bleeds weakly through the windows between lunch and afternoon tea breaks, already long gone on the way home from work.

In the kitchen, she sits in her usual chair, ignoring the empty placemat across from her. Scoops into a bowl *skyr* and out of season blueberries, rotund and aglow with foreign rays of sun. Pours a thin stream of cream over it and eats hungrily, licking the last drops. She looks at her warped reflection in the back of the spoon and takes a deep breath. Tonight, she will bake her mother a cake and whip cream into tall hills of white to accompany the dense flavour of chocolate.

On the bus, the swarming children fill every nook and cranny, and a meek-looking girl is instructed to sit next to her. Trying to unclench her underbelly, she smiles reassuringly at the girl. The windows are fogged up with heat, the radiator fixed, and her fingertips feel blessedly warm. Stroking them over the cold windowpane, she looks outside and sees colour bleeding back into the town.

A Story in English

Hazel

Bear with me as I write this story—in English. Not my first choice. Nor Q's.

I start with Q coming to England, her writing banned by her state, her person banished. Words of her mother tongue churn in her chest, crying to be uttered, to be heard BACK THERE. People ought to know about her rummaged apartment. Her trembling editor. Her asthma attack in solitary confinement. The shadows that followed her everywhere. In her small apartment in Dagenham, generously offered by a fellow member of the diaspora already settled down in London, she smears a chunder of indignation, indictment, and instigation onto scraps of paper. Then she tears them up. To readers BACK THERE, she's already dead, as are these words.

Some other words she doesn't spew out, but cossets in her heart: words of home. I'll show you: 鲜, 秉笔... but wait, these pictograms wouldn't make sense to you, so let's try phonetic spelling. **Xian**, an adjective similar to "delicious", but thicker, steamier, making you want to shut off all senses except taste. All those tastes... they linger in her mouth, just like words. **Bing Bi Zhi Shu**, an idiom (verb) that means, "to write the truth", created by historians over two thousand years ago who faithfully recorded the ruler's vice at the cost of their lives. She's looked up to them since she was a kid. **Xiao**, an adjective/noun that has acquired the bewildering translation "filial piety," the most basic duty of children to their parents and the highest moral achievement anyone can hope for, an observance that allows no lapses. She has failed spectacularly in this regard. Her parents are still BACK THERE, and the best thing she can do for them is to not contact them in any way, lest they be harassed by the police. **Nu Nu**, a noun from the southern dialect used to address little girls, soft and fond in its sound. Q liked to call her daughter Nu Nu again and again as the little girl babbled on her lap, until the divorce. She still loved her husband deeply, but had to push him and their daughter away from her risky activities. Funny. What activities? She wasn't even an activist. Her activities were her words. She tries to hold onto these words and their meanings that nothing can replace. But they hurt. While she's stranded in England, they only point to a lost homeland.

After spending the first few weeks recovering from the shock of the flight, she delves into English books and TV shows. Soon her already fluent English flows much better, and she contemplates a future of publishing in English. But when drunkards pass by her building at night–shouting, chanting, cursing, smashing glass bottles–she mumbles one of the first English words she's learned: "fuck." Fuck them. These aren't my people. These aren't my readers. I don't give a shit about them. Damn it, why am I swearing in English now? Am I so quick to throw away my mother tongue? It's a slippery slope. Before I know it, I'll be thinking and dreaming in English.

I'm going to spare you the details on how Q gets a marketing job and citizenship in the U.K. Perhaps she rents an apartment in the Elephant and Castle: a red-brick building, with ivy covering the walls. I've been to that area. Quite a few Chinese markets. Wouldn't mind living there myself.... Anyway, what I really want to show you are the stacks of manuscripts in her drawers, written in her mother tongue, but you won't be able to understand them. That's the reason why she tucks them away, because you cannot understand, and those who do understand cannot read them. Moreover, she doesn't believe in her words anymore. How ironic! She leaves her home country to seek freedom of expression, but finds her words all rootless and floaty now she has all the freedom in the world. She writes because she has to, so that she can keep going, but is it really possible to produce good work without an intended audience? Many have argued for a positive answer, but I'm not sure. Should she switch to English, and become an "international" writer? Ha, "En-ternational". Or should she write in Chinese anyway, for a small, scattered diaspora and a home readership who might finally acknowledge her after decades?

I've slipped. I've been trying to circumvent the revelation that Q is Chinese because I don't want you to instantly conjure up all the things you think you know about China. Also, if I never mention the exact country, there's less risk for myself, right? But I can't hide from my origin for too long. Neither can Q.

In her eighth year in England, she receives the third-hand news that her father has suffered from a serious stroke—I hate such a cruel plot, but that's not something I can control. Q applies for a visa to go BACK THERE. She's rejected. Three months later, she wakes up one morning breathless, with a stabbing pain in her heart.

Her father has died. She just knows.

Staggering to her desk, Q heaves out her manuscripts. Like burning paper money at a grave, she sets fire to her words in the kitchen sink, Chinese words that she's written to eternalize the home she used to have, to demolish the home that kicks her out, and to recreate a home that's better for all her compatriots. She burns them all. Her tears drop on the cinders. Hissing beams of white smoke.

Q doesn't even realize when the fire alarm is set off. She thinks it's something in her ears: the screams of thousands of people who have lost their loved ones to an oppressive regime. The sound of the Chinese language degenerating into a mishmash of bureaucratese and propaganda, like air leaking from a balloon.

I will also spare you the whole drama with her irritated neighbors. The point is that when the teeth of fire chew up her words, she prays to God, or Heaven, or whatever, to take her mother tongue from her, to let her start anew as a *tabula rasa*. I watch Q collapsing on her bed, and I peel the Chinese from her mind while she's in a lifeless slumber.

That's why this story is written in English.

When Q wakes up, she has really forgotten every single word of her mother tongue. All her memories from BACK THERE have been translated into English. For example, she remembers her daughter calling her while she was in prison, "Mum, I got three red stars today! One for how tidy my desk was, and two for being the first to recite the poem *Drinking on the Lake, First Sunny, Then Rain.*" But she can't hear her daughter's voice saying that. When she dreams of kneeling before her parents, she's only able to say, "I'm so sorry. You've suffered so much because of me." **Xiao** is no longer grilling her. Her parents answer, "Go! Go! Don't let them catch you."

In her twelfth year in England, she publishes her first English novel, *Amnesino,* a fragmented biographical fiction of herself and a few other Chinese writers in exile. She's interviewed them in English, to their surprise, invoking them to relive their experiences in an alien language. The novel is acclaimed as "courageous," "lucid," and "heartbreakingly candid." But she knows it really is craven, confused, and heartbreakingly escapist. What kind of an author is she to abandon her own language? She curses herself for that life-changing prayer she made in despair. "Fuck," "damn," and "bloody hell" roll out of her mouth. She attempts to re-learn Chinese, but it bounces off her head and shatters like her past life.

Another twenty-one years have passed. Q is on her deathbed, her British husband and mixed-race son holding her hands tightly, promising her they will take her ashes BACK THERE. Perhaps I should let her go like this:with all the sweet memories she has acquired in English, vivid and fresh. It isn't a bad way to leave. But I know I wouldn't want to die without remembering. Without remembering, I'd still be haunted by the question "who am I" in the afterworld. I must give 中文 back to her. The legacy of 秉笔直书 must be carried on in 中文. It is the duty of writers to preserve 清白 in 中文 for future generations, even if they have to compromise 孝 and 慈, even if 天下人悠悠之口 is gagged, even if they forever 萍飘蓬转.

At the end of the story，樊阡微笑着对丈夫和儿子说，"It'll be alright"。是啊，她知道会没事的。因为我把中文还给了她。活着不能以之呼号，至少死去有挽歌相送。

The Hamster

Suzanne Enoch

The final straw was when I found a hamster in their bin. I habitually eat cod and chips for supper on Wednesday. Not from that new place with the neon pink sign, but from Stefano's, which is just down at the junction and delicious as ever. *It's important to get the greasy wrapper out of the house or it will attract rats*, Margaret always said. So straight after supper, I emptied the kitchen bin into the wheelie bin. I had just thrown the black bag into the wheelie when I heard scuffling coming from the bin beside mine: number twenty-four's bin.

I opened it, thinking I would have to write to the council about rats, and there was a hamster staring up at me—forlorn, fawn-coloured, and covered in coffee grounds. I had kept a hamster as a childhood pet and have quite a soft spot for them, so I instantly took pity on this unfortunate creature. Clearly it belonged to number twenty-four: the unpleasant, noisy family. There was always some kind of fracas coming from that house. Although I never said anything to them about the noise, or the untidy garden, or the car full of rubbish that I have to pass every day, an animal in the bin is the limit.

I scooped up the hamster, which lay still like a burst tea bag in my hand, and marched to their door. It flitted through my mind that I could just keep the hamster, since I had toyed with the idea of getting another one, but this moment gave me an opportunity to hold them accountable for their actions. I couldn't pass that up.

As I marched up the path, there was all manner of commotion coming from the house as was just par for the course. I ignored it and knocked on the door. A child of about four or five opened it, wiping his runny nose on the back of his sleeve.

'Is your Mother home?'

'Mummy!' screamed the small boy back into the house, his sleeve now noticeably viscous.

Gradually, the noise stopped. A tall, weedy girl of about ten appeared, followed closely by a middle-sized, sour-faced child who looked to be about seven. Eventually, a haggard and wild-haired woman appeared.

I revealed the hamster I was cupping in my hands.

'Is this yours?' I asked

'Buttons!' screamed the watery eyed girl. She reached out to take the hamster, but I moved my hands away.

'We've been looking everywhere for him,' said the taller girl, 'he got out last night.'

'I found him in the bin,' I announced to the mother, and when her eyes widened, I added, 'yes, in the bin. If you didn't want him, there are plenty of places which adopt hamsters.'

'Give him back! He's my hamster!' screamed the middle girl, who I now deduced created most of the perpetual din, whilst the snotty boy laughed.

'Buttons was hiding in the bin!' he gasped.

'I'm so sorry,' said the haggard mother, 'he must've got into the binbag I took out this morning. We've been turning the house upside down looking for him. Is he ok?'

Such a stupid question! 'He's been in the bin all day. He's filthy, and probably cold, and...'

'Well thank you so much for bringing him back,' she said and scooped Buttons right out of my hands where I had been warming him up. Then she smiled and closed the door in my face.

I couldn't believe it. I was livid. Staring at that closed door, I resolved never to cross paths with them again.

The next morning, I began. I started to track their activities so I could avoid them. I would only leave the house after they had left for school and would return home after they were back. At 8:23am, they left for school. The boy pushed the loud girl, and she started to wail. The haggard mum was locking the door, so the tall girl pulled her sister away. When the mother eventually came, she gave the boy a hug. Inexplicable, if you ask me, because she should have given him a wallop for shoving his sister.

I had the afternoon shift at the Cancer Research shop on the high street, and was pleased to find number twenty-four already home when I got back. They were going at each other's throats and although I couldn't tell what they said, through the window I saw a great mound of washing on their sofa. The mother was wearily hanging it on a flimsy airer leant against the wall, but just as fast as she did, the wretched boy was pulling it off. Then the mum picked it up and put it on again. I watched this strange war of attrition until the shouty girl came and closed the curtains. Her face was red and streaked again. But I suppose if I lived with that family, I would cry too.

That evening, I ran out of merlot and felt quite bereft without my evening glass. So I popped out to the corner shop, which is when

I encountered the older girl. She was attempting to heft the wheelie bin through the garden gate and onto the street for collection, but the bin dwarfed her narrow frame and she struggled to pull it up the lip of the curb.

I should have looked before I left the house, of course. I should have checked that the coast was clear. But here I was, caught off guard, and the first words which tumbled from my mind were,

'How's Buttons?'

The girl spoke haltingly, between her wild attempts to yank the bin up.

'He's. Fine. He ate until. We ran out of hamster food.'

'Well, yes, I expect he was hungry.' I said, wondering why I didn't just walk away.

The girl carried on smacking the bin into the step viciously until I couldn't stand it. She was too small for the task.

'That's too heavy for you.' I said to her.

The awful thudding stopped.

'I know!' She shouted, tilting her head up to face me. Her eyes glistening, she started thumping the bin again.

I wasn't going to be spoken to like that and so off I walked. *Be patient with the youngsters*, Margaret's voice rang in my head, but I ignored her. As the repetitive thuds faded into the distance, I thought about that poor hamster, shut in his cage with no more food.

On my way back, I passed number twenty-four. The bin was abandoned inside the gate, and I thought about my unfortunate meeting with the girl. If I were to avoid them, I would have to know quite a lot more about their movements.

That evening, I listened through the wall with a glass like they do in spy films. At first, all I could hear was general complaining and grumbling. But later, I suppose it was after the smaller girl and boy were asleep, a conversation, probably between the tall girl and the mother. It was hard to make out the phrases in amongst all the crying and sniffling, but 'it's all fine' and 'we'll be okay' figured like mantras.

I lay awake most of the night, contemplating the whole dilemma. The poor neglected hamster was probably hungry again by now. Finally, I got up and went for a turn around the block. As I passed number twenty-four, a vision of the tall girl thumping like a headache came to mind. The bin men would be doing their rounds within the next hour, and if the bin wasn't at the curb, it wouldn't be emptied. During the next week, the bin would certainly overflow, and the rats and children would play in the rubbish. Silently, I swung open the gate. In the garden, I collected stray bits of litter which had dropped and popped them into the bin. Much better. Quiet as I could, I lifted the bin up the curb and onto the pavement.

When morning came, I watched at my window as the family spilled from the house. The tall girl and the mother were engaged in a vociferous dispute, which stopped as soon as they saw the bin neatly placed on the street. The mother gasped when she found it empty, prompting the smaller two children to stop poking each other. Looking around the mother almost caught me at the window, but I withdrew. Then the tall girl bumped the bin easily back down the curb into the garden and they all walked quietly off.

The street was peaceful. I pondered as I ate my marmalade toast. There was a pet shop near Cancer Research. I would pop in at lunch time for some hamster food. Later that night, I would leave it on their doorstep.

In the quiet, I heard Margaret's voice. *That's better*, she said.

The Barn

Connie Coneybeer

The Old Avery Barn is falling down.

We hear it in the creaking of the beams as the wind howls through the Petaluma Gap, bringing with it the musty smells of crushed grapes, asphalt, cow shit and dust. We laughed at first at the intrusion of the wind. We squinted through holes in the old aluminum roofing and counted the cobwebs that blocked the sky. It seemed to us the funniest thing in the world that this barn might collapse at any moment.

Now, later, the hay is scratchy beneath our backs and a gentle rustling in the rafters reminds us that we aren't alone. Bats, maybe, or owls, keeping vigilant watch over us strangers. This barn hasn't housed livestock in a generation. We can barely see our hands in front of our faces but our numbers give us a strange sort of confidence in this abandoned building, now home to creatures of the dark. We left our phones in the cars as a sort of solidarity with what had seemed unknown, but now we miss the light.

A moan, as the supports sway ever so slightly; a shriek, as the wind picks up once again; the low rumble of cars passing at the base of the hill. These are the sounds that the Old Avery Barn has grown used to over her years teetering on the age of collapse. We aren't so used to them, yet, but we tell ourselves that by the morning, we'll know them as well as the sirens of our cities. This is a return to our roots.

We shiver and move closer, bundled under an old blanket and masked by the smell of old cow shit and moldy straw. Christ, it's cold. Why didn't anybody tell us it would be cold? We huddle together and hope that the roof will hold just one more night.

There are no signs warning us not to come here, no faded CONDEMNED slapped across the front of the doors in red lettering, no indication that the county intends to bring this old place to the ground. The grand old dame is just one of a million, her name taken from a family that moved away years ago, driven out by the very same suburbia from which we've come. Our parents told us that when most of these barns were built, ranchers navigated by landmarks: stone walls erected to mark the boundaries of their property, stands of eucalyptus dropping sheathes of bark in the wind, family names. Still, we rely on our phones to guide us, even as our reception flickers and our maps freeze.

We drove up the dusty driveway slowly, so we wouldn't hurt the undercarriage of our car, and had to stop twice for the sheep who trundled across our path. They stopped and stared at us like we were the outsiders, like we were the ones who didn't belong out there, where our only marker was the barn, leaning against the relentless gusts. We were lucky it wasn't the rainy season, when our tires would've sunk deep into the mud. The dust we kicked up settled on the grapevines, heavy with unripe fruit. When we reached the barn, the door slid open on rusty hinges, granting us admittance to this secret world.

From the entrance, we could see across the highway a sister-barn, an old dairy, that had finally succumbed to the wind, her legs giving way beneath the tremendous weight of one hundred years of neglect. Her aluminum roof still fluttered, threatened to tear further from the foundation and plummet to the highway below.

The Gap is not kind to these stately barns, timbered and roofed and filled with livestock and life decades ago. Our valley of gently rolling vineyards and oak trees has always hidden a terrible secret: the persistent wind that's sent buildings and cars and carriages tumbling to their demise, generation after generation. Each barn that falls remains motionless, as though defeated. In the Old Avery Barn, we know better.

"It's haunted, you know," we were told once. "That highway—it has a bloody history."

It's hardly a highway, one lane each direction, slicing down the middle of the valley like an unhealed gash, connecting *us* to *them*, the lifeline between our towns, our cities, our metropolises. We'd never thought of a road as being haunted until we looked down on it from above and saw how small the cars seemed against the early evening gusts. How many times had we driven down that road, never noticing the wind except when the car pulled first one direction and then another, looking up from our phones only to glance at the cows and sheep dotting the hills, wondering *who would ever live out here* when we saw the houses and barns and acres and acres and acres of grapes.

When it was light out, we explored every inch of the barn, shrieking with terrified delight as rodents and feral cats scattered at our approach, carefully turning over old planks and fallen beams and leaping away from the long-dead husks of spiders that still clung to their webs.

E.B. MAY 11 1921.

R D L JAN 10 1923

TM JAN 10 1923

They scratched their names into the old planks in big, blocky lettering, confident that the posts and beams would stand against the howling wind. It was one hundred years ago, now, that they were here.

There are more, too, too faded for us to make out, turned to a jumble of barely recognizable shapes by the insistent gnawing of time. In the morning, we will scratch our own initials into the timbers, leave our own mark besides E.B., R D L, and TM. We wonder if the next visitors to the barn will make up our names and stories, inventing romances and tragedies to pass the hours, running their fingers along the time-smoothed ridges left behind by the letters and imagining our hands meeting across time. We wonder if it'll still be standing a century from now.

"Do you think the highway really is haunted?" one of us asks and we're all very, very still as the breeze slips through cracks in the siding, making an almost-human whine that undulates and fades. In that moment, it seems possible—likely, even—that the asphalt, paved and repaved for a hundred years, is supernatural.

Then another of us, lying on their side with their eyes closed, says, "With cows, maybe," and it seems silly that we'd ever dared dream of haunted highways.

The old milk alleys are devoid of livestock now, filled instead with old farm equipment that stinks of oil: rusting tractors and plows, burst tires, empty barrels with burst hoops. There's no hay in the rafters, even though the hay ladder still slides haltingly along its rails; it's piled in the middle of the barn now, where we can climb it to sit and stare and sleep.

We're silent again, listening to our breathing and the wind and the gentle cooing of the owls. Somewhere, a coyote yips, the bark rising to a scream before winding down. A creature scratches around the base of the hay bales and we fall quiet, willing it to investigate, to join us for just this moment. There's hay in our hair, in our clothes, under our fingernails, and there's dust—dust everywhere else, choking us when we try to speak, sticking to the back of our throats, muffling any sound we might hope to make.

One of us moos and the moment is broken. We elbow them in the side, trying not to laugh, trying to hide our regret and the feeling of abrupt loss. Our shared warmth is all that we have in this haunted barn. We shuffle again, jostling each other for the best position under the too-small blanket, arms grabbing for the few pillows we had thought to bring along.

We aren't so far from civilization; the stars are polluted with light from the nearest town, the highway rumbles, a sudden light pierces the darkness as a phone blinks to life—not left in the car, after all. We'll never know this barn as well as the wind that tears away at what human hands built, but we'll do what we have always done and take what we can: pictures, memories, the silence.

The wind groans, the barn creaks, and we slowly fall silent as we drift off, not quite to sleep but to try to reclaim the stillness.

The Old Avery Barn is falling down, but our names are written on her supports.

Save Your Love

 Sofia Reyes Valencia

You close the door behind the two of you. You're in a room with warm lighting. The lamp has a cloth shade with a fringe; the double-size bed has brown and orange accents; the walls are a soft green. Your beloved has messy, Farah Fawcett bangs, and she's crying uncontrollably.

You're trying to hold her in your arms, to soothe her—softly brushing her hair back, wiping at the muddy tracks of mascara making their way down her cheeks. Her foundation has rubbed away too. Susie is so, so pretty. It breaks your heart.

A deep voice announces something from outside the room. Then, a swell of boisterous laughter. She recognizes his voice (of course she does) and breaks into a new wave of tears. If you ever get the chance, you're going to kill Marshall.

Being here isn't helping. The house is small and the walls are thin, and there's no way she actually wants to go back out there without her makeup on. You leave her seated on the floor—her back against the bed, arms around her knees—and make your way to the phone.

"Hi, Mrs. Murphy. Yeah, it's Alex. Is Amber there? Thank you." You notice she's stopped crying in an effort to listen to something going on in the hallway. You listen closely as well. Two pairs of footsteps, that same baritone laugh, *him*, and ... another girl.

"Amber? It's me. Can you come pick us up?" You listen to her speak for a moment, complaining about how late it is.

"Please?" You try not to sound desperate.

You've got the cord between your fingers, twining it around like a small rubber snake seeking warmth. You can hear Amber sigh.

"I'll be there in a sec."

You pull your beloved up gently, rubbing small circles on her back, guiding her to the window. Thank God the Churchwell's live in a bungalow. You pry the pane upwards, kick one leg over the other and land softly on the grass. Then you make sure to help Susie, offering your shoulders for her to hold as she pushes herself off the ledge. You're steady as you catch her, like always.

Both of you are sitting on the curb waiting for Amber to show up. You have one arm slung around Susie's shoulders, and you're not complaining even though her warm tears and mascara seep into the white shoulder of your tee shirt. You recognize those headlights in the distance and stand up, waving your arms, hoping she sees you before she lets out her customary honk. Amber's driven an old Vista Cruiser since you were teenagers. No need to worry about who gets shotgun—the three of you always squish into the front seat. Shoulder to shoulder to shoulder.

You usher Susie into the middle, sharing a look with Amber. Wordlessly, you sit and wrap your arm around Susie's shoulders again. Amber drops her right hand from the steering wheel to link her fingers with Susie's, her thumb lovingly stroking the back of her hand.

"Let's go home, Suze," she murmurs.

You make it to the end of the street when Susie asks you if you still have her purse. "Yeah," you respond gently, sliding it off your shoulder and handing it back. She digs through it, shuffling past multiple items in her search for a small packet of tissues at the bottom. She pulls out the small glass bottle of vodka she's been nursing all night, about an inch of liquid left sloshing at the bottom. She considers it for a while, turning it back and forth to see how it reflects the coppery streetlights above, her fingers playing with the red aluminum screw top. Impulsively, she twists it off and raises the lip of the bottle to her mouth, intent on downing anything left inside. Both you and Amber exclaim, unable to stop her before she licks away the last drop, wiping her mouth with the back of her hand.

"Amber, I need you to turn around—I need to go back to Marshall's house."

"What the hell are you talking about?"

"If I don't do it now, I'm never going to do it."

"Do what?!" she asks, brows scrunched tight in confusion.

Susie lets a beat of silence pass before finally whispering, "Tell him how I feel."

"Oh Susie, no."

"Please? Amber. *Please.*"

Even though you can feel your gut twisting in jealousy, you make a point of remaining expressionless. Susie shifts to look at you, holding both of your hands in hers.

"Lex, if I don't do this now, I'm never going to do it."

You don't look at either of them when you speak to Amber, "I guess we're going back to Marshall's." You're quiet as you say this, and you know Amber notices. You appreciate it when she doesn't mention it.

Instead, she sighs and turns the car around. You ride in silence until the silhouette of his house appears to your left.

"No! Wait. Wait, keep going. I can't do this."

"What?!" Amber nearly stomps on the brakes.

"No, I mean, I *can* do this. I just. I can't do it now. Drive up and down the block a few times. I- I need to think about what I'm going to say."

"What you're going to say? Suze, you've been in love with him since middle school—you've spent hours of our time together talking about what you'd say!" Your voice nearly comes out as a growl.

"I know, but it's not that easy. You don't know what it's like!"

"Oh, I don't?" You hate looking at her like this—a sneer on your face and anger in your heart.

"No! Not like me and Marshall. I just need a little bit of time to work up my nerve."

She takes your hands again, looking between the two of you, eyes shining with hope.

Your heart is pounding. One beat. Two. You sigh, "Fine, whatever."

"Lexi, are you sure—" Amber's hand hovers above the gear shift.

"Let's just give her a few minutes." You're still holding Suzie's hand, but you can't look at either of them.

The three of you spend an eternity rolling up and down Marshall's street.

"Marshall, I know this will sound sudden—no. Marshall Churchwell, I've known since that day in Miss Kirkpatrick's class when you doodled a smiley face onto my homework—Marsh, I—"

She pulls her hand away from yours and instead wraps them

around her knees again, thinking silently. Intensely. Then finally, "Okay, I think I've got it."

Amber pulls up to Marshall's driveway. You open the door, moving to get out, but Susie simply swings her leg over your hips, shimmying out of her position in the middle. You share a look, and you can see the glimmer of something sparkling in her eyes. She stands up straight and smoothes down the front of her jeans.

"How do I look?"

You stare at her in the moonlight. You try not to cry in frustration.

"Lex?"

You swallow.

"Good. You look ... good."

She nods once, suddenly confident, definitely feeling those last few gulps of vodka.

"Hey, Susie?"

She turns back around to you. "Yeah?"

"You don't have to do this." You grasp her hand and hope it's enough for her to read between the lines. "Not right now. We could, we could just go home. Stop by the diner for some milkshakes on the way. Forget about this stupid party?" *Forget about stupid Marshall.*

To your surprise, she does think about it for a second. But there's still that sparkle in her eye when she looks back up, smiling a little sadly.

"If I don't do this now..."

You nod at her once, "Okay." Your voice is soft when you let her hand go.

You're still looking at one another, stuck in this moment, fragile as a soap bubble.

"You're right, you know." You look away from her, up to the space above her head, "I don't think I would ever have the nerve to do something like this."

She huffs out a nervous laugh, "It's more about being stupid than it is about being brave, I think."

"Well, whatever it is, Amber and I will be waiting right here. For better or worse."

You smile at her encouragingly. It's genuine. She smiles back before turning and walking up to the house.

You look away and shut the door. Amber scoots towards you and (like a mirror, like a time delay) she wraps her arm around the back of your shoulders. You lean into her, and she kisses your temple.

"I know."

You press your head into the crook of her arm, taking a deep, almost angry breath. She rubs her hand up and down your arm. It's two a.m., and you've never felt so tired.

"I know."

The Boring Bits

Nicholas Alter

The night grandpa slew his first dragon, he had a smoke. He cracked an egg on one of her scales and fried it over-easy. The yolk was bright as sunlight, he told me, the whites so rich he couldn't finish the last bite. Not quite as spicy as Phoenix eggs, but far more filling given their size. He would know. He was one of the only people on Earth who'd tasted both.

He was an impressive man, my grandfather. A traveling salesman by trade, he dealt in the most obscure, the most incredible. He always wore a slim-cut tweed suit that made him seem taller than any man I'd ever seen. The weave was spun from the wool of a sea goat. He swore the fibers were tough enough to stop a bullet, which was plenty strong given the prey he hunted only had teeth and claws and horns. On one hip he kept a silver sword, on the other was a pistol engraved with druidic runes. I never saw him without the tools of his trade. He often let me hold them when mom wasn't looking. He'd give me a conspiratorial wink and say, "This is just between us, buddy."

Every time he visited, he brought home gifts—dragon eggs or were-bear claws, oni horns or basilisk fangs, selkie pelts, even unicorn meat for mom to cook up. Once, he smuggled out an eel from Atlantis; a shiny, wriggling thing he handed to me in a plastic bag, like a goldfish I could get from the state fair.

We would see him at least once a year, sometimes twice if we were lucky. I relished every visit, not because of the gifts (although I cherish the few I still have) but because of the endless stories he told.

"Did I ever tell you about the time..."

That was how they started. He would lean back in his chair and glance up at the ceiling. I would sit cross-legged on the floor in front of the fireplace, staring up at him like he was an old sage expounding lessons.

He had hunted goblins, ridden with centaurs, tracked a jacka-lope for a hundred miles. Aboard a ship in the South China Sea, he fended off a kraken with a crew of only twenty men. He'd been all over the world. He visited King Arthur's grave—said the apples on Avalon were even sweeter than those he ate in Eden. In Jotunheim he communed with the giants and in Alfheim he danced with elves. He traded sea shells with mermaids, mushrooms with gnomes, a ghillie suit to Bigfoot. He wrestled a kelpie, strapped a saddle to its back, and rode it to market.

When he was young (and a little more bold), he sold a pair of mountain trolls their own dung disguised as handmade sausages. He showed me the scar on his ankle where they hog tied him up over the fire.

Once, he compared for me the song of a harpy to that of a siren. "Harpies sing like pop stars," he said, "sirens are more like opera singers."

For some reason, that always stuck with me.

When I was five or six, he shared a meal with a vampire, watched the man tear into a live pig right there at the dinner table. Mom got mad at him for sharing that story, said I was too young. I promised I could handle it, but truthfully, I didn't sleep for at least a week.

Just before he got sick, he'd seen a qilin atop the Kunlun Mountains overlooking Shangri-La. He stumbled upon the creature as it drank from a cerulean pool beneath a grove of peach trees. "Part horse, part dragon," he whispered, "with azure scales and a mane of flaming fur." Her antlers were a crimson gold, her long legs tufted in silver hairs, her tail formed wisps of powdered snow. As she raised her head from the pool, he saw in her eyes deep wells of knowledge.

When I asked him if he brought those antlers back with him, if each azure scale was worth its weight in gold, he shook his head.

"There are certain things in this world too benevolent to disturb. They say spotting a qilin heralds the coming of a great sage. Or his end. Isn't that incredible, buddy?"

In less than a year, he was bedridden. Pancreatic cancer— virtually untreatable. A sickness like that just lies in wait until there's nothing you can do about it (he wasn't the kind of man to go in for yearly checkups).

When mom took me to the hospital to visit, he was a shrunken thing, pale as the vampire he'd once described to me. His sword and pistol were propped up in the corner of his hospital room, and I remember thinking that they looked more like decorations than tools. I was a little older then, almost ten. Old enough to understand, but not quite old enough to process everything.

Mom left us alone. I sat beside him in a squeaky plastic chair. I could tell he was glad to see me, and that made it easier to look at him. The whites of his eyes were a murky yellow, his hair had fallen out in clumps, his fingernails were chipped. For a moment, I wondered how he would describe a creature like him.

"Did I ever tell you about the time I found El Dorado?" he began, but he couldn't finish the story. A nurse came in and fiddled with something on the monitor.

"Sorry, buddy." He wouldn't look at me, just glanced up at the ceiling like he had dozens of times before. Eventually, he sighed. "I thought I'd have more time."

I didn't understand. He'd seen so much, been to unimaginable places! He conquered a thousand legends, brought home a thousand stories, sold to kings and queens and millionaires. When I told him I wished I could live a life just as adventurous, he frowned, patted my hand.

"Just try not to leave out the boring bits."

On the ride home, I asked mom what he meant by that. "The boring bits?" she scoffed. "Your grandfather's never been satisfied."

Except he always seemed so satisfied—well dressed, a smile on his face. It wasn't until I was much older that I better understood my mother's response: she simply didn't see him the same way I did.

It's funny, when you're a kid, it's hard to recognize that the adults in your life are human too, just as capable of experiencing the same turbulent emotions you are. That they have a past you may never know—a whole *life that used to be* long before you even existed. For a kid, well, that's just inconceivable. Parents, grandparents, they're protectors first and foremost, givers of food and shelter, of love and stories. To think they've struggled would make them fallible, and if they're fallible, how can they protect you?

Years after he died, on a trip home from college, I helped mom organize her attic. We sorted through too many boxes to count. Old baby clothes and stuffed animals. Three bookshelves of books. Albums with family photos. Documents long past keeping. All my old toys.

In the back left corner, stuffed behind an old dresser, I found a box labeled *Treasures*. It was filled with jewels and golden trinkets. When I showed it to my mother, she smiled a little. We set out the treasures one by one on the floor. She held them gingerly as if they all might crumble into dust with too tight a grip. There was a story associated with each one, a place grandpa had been or a monster he had defeated. After we had touched them all, spent some time talking about grandpa and the way he used to go on and on, she put the treasures back in the box.

We sat there silently for a moment, and then she said, "You know, I never wanted any jewels."

I can't help but think of my grandfather as an impressive man, but nobody is just one single thing. I'm glad I got to know him, I'm just not sure he ever really got to know me. If I could talk to him now, I wonder what I would say. I haven't slayed any beasts, never rode a unicorn, never heard a harpy's song. I find my eggs at the supermarket, not in a dragon's den way up in the mountains. I watch too much TV and like to go to the movies with my friends. I visit mom on the weekends, and we often just spend our time reading together by the fire. I'm happy to embrace the boring bits.

Through the Fairy Glen

Sanna Waern

My grandma disappeared the day before she was supposed to move into the nursing home.

It was the middle of October and she had just turned eighty-nine. The last couple of weeks, my dad and I had spent a lot of time helping her sort through everything that she and my grandpa had collected over the years. She had become increasingly forgetful since he died and their old house, poorly heated and prone to dampness, was no longer safe for her. For years, she had insisted that she was still well enough to live by herself; then came the incidents where she forgot to turn the cooker off or accidentally left a tea light burning overnight. She began to talk about my grandpa as if he was still alive, and she would get my dad and I mixed up. After many conversations with my dad and her doctors, she reluctantly agreed to move out.

It was strange to see my grandma's house boxed up and empty. I understood why she was so hesitant about the move. She had always lived in that house, since way before I was born. When I was small and visited my grandparents in the summers, my grandma would take me on walks in the country park to see the ruins of the gunpowder mills. Muttering about restless spirits lying in wait, she would verge off the path and into the low canopy of aspen and willow. She always brought small bottles of milk, rum, and honey with her and would carefully place these in the depths of the woods by the roots of a great hawthorn tree.

'What are you doing?' I had asked her, only once, when I was about six or seven years old.

'They'll cause trouble if we don't feed them,' my grandma said. Her voice, uncharacteristically solemn, startled me. I could tell that she was being serious.

'Who?' I asked.

She just smiled at me. 'The guid folk. The *fairies*. They might steal us away if we don't show our good manners.'

Dad and I drove down to her house that morning to help her move the last few things. As we knocked on the door, though, it silently swung open. My dad and I exchanged glances of prompt worry, then went inside.

The smell of my grandma's Italian perfume—with subtle notes of bergamot and peach—lingered in the rooms, but she was nowhere to be found. On the mantelpiece in the living room stood her quietly murmuring radio. I walked into the kitchen and touched the half-drunk cup of tea on the table. It was cold.

Except for the landline, my grandma had no phone. My dad decided to go down the street and check if any of the neighbours had seen her. I had a look around the house. Around the corner was the shed in which my grandparents kept bikes, rods, and crabline. There was a tiny garden in the back, now grown wild with brambles and stinging nettles. Tangles of bindweed clung to the old trunk of the apple tree. I sat down on the front steps, waiting.

We weren't going to keep much of my grandma's stuff. Dad had no interest in her furniture, the vintage crockery, nor her old diaries, and I simply had no space for it. I shared a flat with four others in Dalry. There was barely enough room for us to breathe.

I went back into the house to have another look around. The jar of loose change still stood on the telephone table in the hall; whenever we went to the shallow cave by the beach, she pressed pennies into the cracks of the rock for good luck. My grandpa had smoked his pipe and said little. Whenever I doubted my grandma and I looked over at him, he just smiled and gave me a reassuring nod.

It felt like she was still here, somewhere. Perhaps it was the iron nails hammered into the bedframe, or the dried primroses spread over the windowsills.

I realised then that my grandma's walking cane was gone. My grandma had severe osteoarthritis. She couldn't get far without her cane.

I called my dad once, twice, three times, but he didn't pick up. I texted him instead, saying, *I wonder if she has gone for a walk?* Then, I sent another message, adding, *I'll go check for her by the mills.*

Autumn tugged the leaves from the trees as I made my way down to the country park. It was unlikely that my grandma would have been able to walk down to the woods without help, but I couldn't shake the idea. The woods were muddy and quiet, with only the occasional dog-walker passing me on the wide path. Everywhere, there were moss-covered birch trees and broad buckler ferns. Along the path ran a little brook that crept along the tangled roots of trees and loose rocks, sometimes disappearing entirely beneath patches of moss.

After I passed the ruins of the gunpowder mills, I verged off the path, like my grandma had shown me so many times before. It was a bit of a scramble to get down the slope. I nearly fell over as I slipped on the wet leaves.

'Grandma?' I called out once I reached the bottom and steadied myself.

I called out again. My voice sounded small. The woods pressed upon me, tall and knowing. I walked slowly, listening for sounds of people. Soon I reached the big hawthorn tree. Red clusters of ripe berries hung on the branches. I couldn't see any offerings near the tree; there were no small bottles at all, neither full nor empty.

I kept walking and called out for her again.

All of a sudden, I could smell her perfume. Bergamot and peach. My throat went dry. Then I saw it, the bronze of it glinting in the sun: her walking cane, half-hidden under the shrubs. It looked like it had been there for some time. I pulled the cane up through the leaves of the rush. I looked around, expecting—and hoping—to catch a glimpse of her red jacket somewhere nearby.

A strange sense of anxiety creeped over me then—the unmistakable feeling of being watched. I looked around, searching for people or animals in-between the trees. I couldn't see anyone. The wind picked up. Something seemed to draw near, quickly, and before I had time to think I felt a sharp stab of pain on my left ankle. Pulling my trouser leg up slightly, I noticed a couple of pinpricks of blood. Looking closer, I saw a half-moon of tiny punctures beginning to appear.

They were tooth marks.

With this, I felt a surge of adrenaline, and I turned right around and began running up the slope and back to the path. The bite-mark made my ankle sting. I wasn't sure what had happened. I just knew I needed to get out of there.

My dad was back in my grandma's house when I returned. When he saw my grandma's cane, he called the police. In the following weeks, the police asked the public to be on the lookout, and a search-and-rescue team helped us look for my grandma in the woods and villages around Roslin. Her body is still missing, and she's still on the police's Missing Persons page. The photograph is one I took of her on her last birthday.

I have never said anything about the fairy glen to the police. I took them there, of course, as they wanted to see where I had found the cane. I made sure to keep iron nails in my pocket and when no one was looking, I left a couple of small offering bottles by the hawthorn tree. Silly, you might think, but it helped me put my mind to rest, at least for a little bit.

I have never told anyone about the fairy glen. I seriously doubt they would have believed me. Criminal investigations have no room for magic. The police rely on facts, on evidence. I haven't even told my dad. He had always seen my grandma's superstitions as part of her eccentricism, and never believed a word she had to say about fairies or the other creatures of the lore.

I don't go back to the woods near the old mills anymore.

You're probably thinking I must have imagined it. Could it possibly have been a dream? No. If I ever doubt myself all I need to do is cast a glance down my leg. Because on my ankle is a small, glossy scar—like a sliver of a crescent moon.

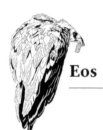

Eos

Tara Troiano

I would like to tell you a story. There are two characters, maybe three: a bird. A man. A god? I play the bird, the vulture. I was hand chosen by Zeus, picked for my appetite. The man plays himself: the damned, the chained. Prometheus. The god lurks in the wings.

The first act is a ballet. A violent dance: muscles ache, limbs stretch. The steps were choreographed long ago by someone else. The music is as old as time. The first three years are without melody. The timpani beats steadily.

Every morning, as the Earth unravels on its spool, I wait until I feel that familiar tug of fate. When hunger stirs, I fly to the rock atop the mountain. He is chained there, bare-chested, waiting for me. As he kneels against stone, his teeth grind into dust. As I dig through his sun-roasted flesh for the only thing that will quell my appetite, the first rays of dawn spill over the horizon. His liver is the antidote to my craving.

Time goes on. Our matinee continues.

For me, a meal. For him, a punishment. We are exiled to our own minds. By which I mean, we are strangers. Seasons pass around us. At first, as I feast, his blood drips onto rock. Then it falls onto browning leaves, then snow. Our stage rotates around the sun. His blood falls to the earth. It is rhythmic, a heartbeat.

Drip. drip. Drip. drip.

Come spring, the blood has nurtured a patch of wildflowers.

It is a ballet, remember. And we were each born to dance. We repeat the movements as though it is the first time. Every dip and turn is discovered over again: the hunger in my eyes, the agony on his face, the desperation in his cries. It is palpable in every show. The audience must be satisfied. We cannot disappoint.

His character is a tragic one. He plays it well. When he braces against the chains that tether him to the rock, his muscles ripple. Dancers are athletes at their core. As I dig through his side, he grunts and braces and thrashes. He knows his fate, but cannot help but fight it.

I do not mind my role. It is better than his. I am glad to no longer scavenge, and it is warm inside his belly.

But then it all changes.

He startles me into fear, and the timpani into silence, when he screams, "WHY MUST YOU HURT ME?"

And while I assume his words are aimed at the heavens, he repeats them again as a whisper only I can hear.

I pause my feast. It is, after all, a meal that does not grow cold. I perch on his shoulder, my beak slick with blood.

"Why must you hurt me?"

"It is because I am hungry," I respond.

He nods. A drop of sweat falls from his matted hair. The orchestra swells, the strings shiver.

"I must make for a gruesome meal."

My stomach groans in objection.

"Carry on," he says. But I resist the hunger pangs, if only for a moment.

I look at the mess I've created at his feet. The tangle of organs and flakes of skin. The puddle of crumbs and morsels.

I would like to tell you a story. There are four characters, maybe six: a bird. A man. A god. The Fates. I play the bird, but the role is growing stale. He plays himself, although I wish he would not. The second act is a comedy, a bad one. The audience remains silent.

I bring him nuts and berries from the fields. In the afternoon, I drop them into his mouth.

I learn which are his favorite by the way his eyes flutter close at the taste of a blackberry or pomegranate seed. I hunt for the firmest ones, the ones the thorny bush is not yet ready to relinquish.

The berries stain his skin, but it is all the same. Blood. Piss. Berries. When he sees me flying over the mountain, the sun safely below its peak, bearing the gifts of the vine, he does not flinch.

"What is your name?" he asks one evening as I drip water into his mouth. It falls over his lip and down his chin.

I shrug. I was not given a name in the script.

"I will call you Eos."

I repeat the word in my head as I fly home.

It is strange. Now that I am telling the story, it is in my power to mold the events how I please, but I cannot help making it about him. It is he who has the golden hair and pleading eyes. A voice that pierces through the morning fog like rays of light. There are some characters to whom stories latch on and hold fast. No, I must try harder. I must wrestle the words until they submit. I must untangle the lines.

I bring leaves and branches and feathers: offerings to a fallen god. I place them under his knees, a nest to keep him warm. How strange it is to dull the pain you inflict.

"Hello Eos, give me your worst," he says each morning.

We both know there is nothing else I can give.

Afterwards, as I perch on his shoulder, he asks me what it feels like to fly.

"I suppose it is how you feel to run."

"I have not run in years. Perhaps my legs have forgotten."

His cheek twitches; there is an itch on his face. I brush my beak against it, and he closes his eyes.

"What would you do if you could no longer fly?"

I would starve.

I do not tell him, but I believe I would like that very much.

As he sleeps, I hunt field mice. I do everything I can to quell my appetite. I eat grasses until my mouth fills with bile. I drink ale until my cave spins around me. But no matter what, in the morning, my stomach growls.

I wish to tell you a story. There are two characters: A bird. A man. I play the man. I play the man. Please, let me be the man. Just once, let me suffer his fate.

The curtains do not rise.

No, it cannot be.

I do not want him to be there forever. But I am not prepared for the morning my stomach does not rouse me from sleep. By the time I arrive at the mountain top, the sun has reached its peak, and the rock is empty.

The narrator announces that the god's wrath has burnt off like the morning sun. Zeus is satiated by Prometheus's pain. But although the man is released from his fate, it haunts him, it haunts me. My stomach does not groan as it once did. But gods, I starve.

I would like to tell you a story. It has been centuries since it began. There are five, six, seven billion characters. It is a tragedy.

Each morning I fly to the fence that circles the cottage he now lives in. It is small and sturdy. There is a garden round the back. Nothing chains him to the house, but he stays there, nonetheless. I watch him through the windows.

At first, he still cannot stand the daylight. He sleeps until evening, nestled under blankets.

Once the sun has set, he stands. He is taller than I remember. His hair is thicker than I thought. He eats and drinks, but he keeps his arms close to his chest. He lurches at the sound of flapping wings.

The story goes on. The world grows around him. The sun sets on the days of heroes and monsters. The old gods slumber.

He works in the fields. Then in the shipyards. Then in the factories.

The dancers' joints grow stiff. The violinists' bows fray. The mountain top remains empty. There are wars and famines and fires.

Now he works in an office. He charms clients and lifts weights. I watch from my fence as he awakens in the morning. There is a woman tangled in his nest of blankets. He kisses her forehead and buttons a shirt over his chest. On his stomach, under tufts of hair, is a scar.

I hear that he got a dog. A dog is no better than a bird. He asks it to speak, but it cannot. A dog is a useless thing, but at least it does not cause him pain.

I wonder what name he gave it.

When I return to the house, he is chasing the dog around the yard. He lunges and runs alongside it. The dog drools from its mouth. It makes a puddle at his feet. He does not seem to mind.

Through the window, I watch his small family eat dinner. Steam rises off their food. He finishes two plates and lets the dog lick the rest.

One day he will have a son who will fall and scrape his knees. The man will bandage those wounds with a steady hand. One day he will have a daughter whose stomach growls. The man will feed her berries until her tongue is purple.

He will not tell his children about his time on the mountain top. If I get my way, he will not remember the steps to that dance, the chords to that overture. I try with my everything to steal that story from his mind. To lift it off his shoulders. To tell it as a play, a comedy, a tragedy, a romance, a riddle, over and over again until the story is only mine to bear.

For now, he eats.

The man dips his fork into his wife's plate. She jokes about his appetite. She brushes an eyelash from his cheek, and he smiles. There are dimples on his cheeks. I have never seen them before. They startle me, and I fly away.

EXCERPTS

The Reaper

Charlie Chapman

Rain fell in pleats over London, driving the scattered commuters beneath bus stops and covered alleys. They looked up at the sky with scorn, complaining as loudly as Londoners ever dared to. Strangers muttered curses and locked eyes across the pavement, begrudgingly united for a fleeting instant by their shared misfortune.

To be stuck in a downpour on a Tuesday evening was a kind of misfortune, to be sure. But it was also a privilege—the privilege to be inconvenienced, to have a structure, a mutability; a state of affairs to be disrupted in the first place. This was not a privilege the Reaper enjoyed. Rain skimmed off the edge of his wide-brimmed hat and landed unnoticed by his feet. It bounced off the folds of his black felt overcoat, repelled by strands of his dark, waxy hair.

Misfortune was such a singularly human phenomenon, he thought, watching commuters scurry like ants across the street. A human life was so uncertain, so mercurial, as to be affected by a great many things in such a short span of time. There must have been a time when he too was so affected, dependent on things like the beating of his pulse and the weather. But it was so long ago now that he could not remember the feeling—nor much of his former life at all.

There was another reason that the midweek rain was unfortunate; for an evening downpour could double, even triple the hand he was dealt—the many cards that would lead the Reaper to his clients. Even now he could feel them growing heavier in his pocket, the weight of exactly one life for each Jack, Ace or Queen that materialised at his side.

He was running his thumb over one card in particular when the tell-tale screech of tyres cut through the din, accompanied by the sound of shattered glass and the whoosh of a final breath. The mortals went on rushing to and fro, ignorant of the man in black or the stack of cards in his pocket.

The Reaper sighed, stepping out onto the slick tarmac toward the motorbike which had begun to careen wildly off-course across the street. "All this for a little bit of rain."

*

"David Marson."

The man looked up, aghast.

He was young, young enough not to have decided the shape of his life yet. Pale hair curled with boyish innocence on his brow, and in his wallet was tucked a picture of the girl he hoped someday to marry. Details such as these did not move the Reaper any longer, but they demanded to be noticed. When it came to souls, the tokens of a life not yet lived stood out like blank spaces on a page.

The young man blinked. Once, and then again. "I'm sorry?"

"David Oliver Marson. Born in Carlisle, currently in residence at Dalworth Place. Five feet and eight inches, twelve and a half stone—"

"Yes, that's me." He shifted to his knees on the tarmac, flustered. "How did you know all that?"

The Reaper held up a scarlet Jack of Hearts.

His client looked between him and the Jack, frowning. "That's just a playing card."

"Of course." The Reaper gestured to the wreckage of the bike several yards away. "At exactly five fifty-six p.m., on Tuesday the eighth, the deceased—David Marson—became the victim of a collision, resulting in a punctured lung and several fractures in his spine."

The young man's face fell slack as the Reaper reeled off the details on the back of the card. He twisted, staring at the tangle of steel and rubber in the road, hands resting on his knees in tight fists. The scent of rain on concrete hung heavy in the air, pierced only by the wailing of the ambulance that had come too late. The police were stringing hazard tape across the crash, beneath which could be seen a pale hand jutting limply through the smoke.

"You mean, that's—" He turned back to the Reaper and paused, noticing the overcoat, the hat, the way the onlookers were staring past him—through him. "You mean to say, I'm—"

"Precisely." The Reaper stepped backwards, and the crowd seemed to melt around him. "If you'll please follow me."

David Marson peered up at the stern, pallid face beneath the hat's brim. "Who are you?"

The Reaper attempted something like a smile, though judging by the look of horror it prompted from his client, he assumed it'd fallen somewhat short of convincing. Dropping the grimace, he simply answered, "I'm a servant of Death."

"Death? As in ... like, death itself?"

"Yes." The Reaper and his client stared at one another for a long moment. The young man was still kneeling on the tarmac—he looked like he'd just been slapped.

"Oh," he said, a little stupidly. "Right then. Lead the way."

Leaving behind the sirens and the scent of burning rubber, the Reaper turned and began to weave stiffly between the commuters in the downpour. He didn't wait to see if David followed. They always did.

The gathered pedestrians ducked in and out of their way, but the Reaper's boots marched silently on. They were consumed entirely by the incident, that uniquely mortal fascination with the tragic and grotesque. Wide eyes blinked rapidly in an ocean around them, averse to the sting of smoke and tragedy. Whispered condolences muddied the air, though a few floated into earshot.

"Looks like a motorbike," came a gruff old voice. "Bloody death traps, those things."

"I hope everyone's alright," murmured one, craning to catch a glimpse through the umbrellas and anoraks. "Looks pretty nasty."

"He must've been drinking," scoffed another, this one closer.

"No! I hadn't!"

David had stopped in front of the man, a pot-bellied grump scowling through him at the wreckage beyond. "Hey! I'm talking to you—"

Cold, pale fingers clamped around his wrist, and David looked up in shock—perhaps because the Reaper had just reached through a passing boy's head. Or perhaps he had finally noticed that he couldn't feel it—not the hand, the rain, nor anything else, for that matter.

The Reaper tugged him onwards. "That man can't see you. Nor me," he explained, as he had done a thousand times before. "Nor does he care whether you were really drinking or not."

His client shuffled on the pavement before giving in, though not without a parting glare at the offender. "I knew that," he mumbled, following the Reaper out the other end of the crowd.

It was instinct that made David swerve when they crossed the road. Though it hadn't done his client much good, the vestige of that mortal instinct to survive was still so strong that David could not comprehend the traffic buzzing through them. When the crash was little more than a pillar of smoke in the distance, the Reaper pulled them to a halt beside the back door of an off-license.

The traffic crawled slowly at their backs as David stared quizzically at his companion.

"Is ... is this it?"

The Reaper cocked his head. "Almost."

David took in the muted grey exterior and peeling paint sign for Holloway Wine & Beer and wrinkled his nose. "I was expecting something ... nicer."

Everyone did. But the entrance to the Afterlife could not be wreathed in pearly white silk, nor heralded by winged angels, or else the mortals might get in. Besides, Death had never been one for excess, and the Reaper himself preferred it this way—unassuming, unobtrusive. As if death was just another door.

His client seemed hesitant—he was shifting his weight, patting his pockets. As though he could feel the absence of his wallet, of the photograph that never left his side. His pockets were empty, but the Reaper's were not; his coat hung lopsided across his shoulders, a heavy stack of cards weighing down one side.

There were more souls than David, more corpses in the rain.

The Reaper leaned into the fire escape, both hands on the bar as the door bowed inward with a heavy iron groan.

"Wait—"

David had one hand outstretched, but he was facing the road, peering through the rain as though expecting something—or someone—to emerge from the fog.

"Yes?"

He turned halfway, neck bent and eyes downcast. He had adopted the death mask, the expression all his clients wore to meet their end. It was somewhere between longing and regret, a hundred nuanced shades of anguish that was their right as humans to feel in their final moments, with that uniquely mortal intensity. The Reaper was incapable of imagining who David thought he'd find on the side of the A1, what piece of his former life he hoped would come bounding out of the traffic. But he knew that look well enough not to argue as he stepped through the door.

He did not wait for David. He would come in his own time.

One Hundred Winters

Anne-Marie Saich

On the morning of the ship's arrival, Inge repeats her daily routine on the roof of the station. The wind is calmer, the salt the same. Pressure is dropping. Radiation levels are unremarkable. Short-comms are active, but no-one from the village has reached out. Up the rungs, she hooks one leg around the satellite mast to lean around and get a glimpse of the south beach. Clear of debris again. Bobbing by the pier on the east beach is her barge, unharmed by the last storm and empty for today's crates.

Indoors, she copies the aerial readings into her log. A screen above her desk is receiving from the satellite, which has been skating above the south pole all morning. Inge swings the screen down from the wall. With an eye still on her log, she types out a message.

INQUIRY #8854
OFF-SHORE. RADIO ACTIVE, SECURE.
TRANSLATION: NO
SENDER ID: It's me, S. I don't have my card on me.
CONTENT: Landing is clear. Watch for the winds, my flags are picking up the dregs of a storm still.

She leans back and folds her hands on her stomach. Her eyes rest on the edge of a window. There's salt building up again like frost. The screen chirps. A response lights up the lower half and flickers; Inge kicks at the cables plugged under her desk until the text stabilises.

RADIO MESSAGE #671
TRANSLATION: NO
SENDER ID: VALIDATED
CONTENT: It's always good to hear you. I've three crates for the village and one for you. And if you have any batteries ready to go, I'll happily take them off your hands. Stay safe down there.

With time to spare, Inge checks the shed. Four batteries are charged and upright by the door. She clears the field of any loose rocks and clumps of flora that could be caught in exhausts or sent up into flames. One last survey, another greeting signal to the satellite to stabilise Sylvester's entry readings, and she finally hears the rumble.

She crouches below a window to watch the sky. There, in the middle of the clouds, is a light like a candle behind a curtain. The rumble still only sounds like thunder, but it already rattles the glass. Slowly, the clouds split. It's a small opening, brief, like an eye blinking, but enough for Inge to catch a rare glimpse of the broad blue curve of their gas giant. Then the clouds close and the sky's all grey again. As the noise of its engine rises to an almost unbearable roar, Sylvester's ship, broad like any creature bred to carry cargo, lowers itself slow and heavy and careful toward the centre of the field. Whatever brave wisps of grass had been growing between the cracks out there are being turned to a fine dust.

Inge waits by the door until her ears stop ringing and she can hear the wind again . Then, she takes the stairs down to the shed and gets to work rolling the first battery outside and across the field. The rock warms the soles of her boots. When she's halfway to the ship, the crew door opens.

"Inge!" The stomp of Sylvester's descent down the metal stepway rattles something in the ship's creaky hull. "You have my battery!"

"Don't you go thinking I'd let you down," she pants, and gives the battery enough of a shove to send it clattering across the plates of stone toward Sylvester's boots. "Only the best."

Sylvester grins his big, bearded grin, folding the thin blue tubes resting on his cheeks that feed him his diet of air. "I always knew I was special to someone," he says. "Now get over here."

His hair is even thinner and paler than the last time she saw him. The ancient tattoo on the back of his hand of a tiny woman pointing toward his knuckles is about as faded.Sylvester helps her lift the battery over the empty socket inside the ship's lower deck. It smells like dust, wood, and ozone down here. The dark wooden walls make the place feel small but warm.

"A storm?" he asks. "Anything broken?"

"No, no. I haven't heard from the village, and the short-comms are operational, so they have it under control." Inge gives the battery's shell a thump to knock it into place. The three lights indicating full capacity, operation, and stability light up. "A storm that strong will fill... ten batteries, if you give us time."

"And the storm didn't bring you any grief at all?"

"No," she lies.

Sylvester scratches his neck. "I'll take the rest of your spare batteries. I've space for seven, beside those crates."

"Olive is training her niece now," says Inge as she rolls the next battery over to the ship. Sylvester walks beside her. "Their workshop was damaged by a small slide last season, but they've been helped by, uh, Mylo and Hornfel. Do you remember them, the ones who almost sunk my barge? Two weeks and Olive's turbines were spinning again. Anyway, that niece is a wild thing. Her batteries might just be pure storm."

Sylvester waits until the last battery is loaded, and the last crate is dropped by the station's door before saying, "I'm retiring this season."

His eyes are getting bad, he says, too bad to risk being at the helm for much longer. Plus, the rattle of re-entry is really starting to ache. His last delivery will be to the Silver Moon because that was his first delivery job, forty years ago.

"I'm sixty-two. I've been old for as long as you've known me." Sylvester grins and wrinkles his air supply again. "Lightspeed can only keep you young so long."

Inge shrugs. She stares at the pin on his collar, a gold arrow for an experienced helmsman. "I'll miss you."

"I should damn hope so."

"For as much as it's worth, we age slower than anyone else in the system, being so close to that star. You could lose a fortnight with every hundred winters spent here."

Sylvester laughs. "If only I had your lungs."

"Oh, I don't know. The off-shore look always suited you."

Inge spends so little time thinking about air. Wind, water, rock, lightning, of course, always. Air is the one problem she's never had. Whoever takes up this station after her will likely be a local too, with lungs that won't scar within a few months of breathing the moon's caustic air. This place has too bad a reputation to attract someone from offshore anyway.

The idea of hosting guests from other planets had once lit her mind on fire (would they find the island and its critical role as Alacrity's only space-port impressive? She'd hoped so) before the reality of this moon's isolation had dawned on her less than a year in. The only new faces she sees are the babies of villagers.

"Those were the niece's then, were they?" Sylvester asks and points a thumb to the ship. "Pure storm."

"The one I plugged in is, yes."

"Good."

"Do you know if you'll pass here again?"

"It's a small chance. I know they've found someone good to take up my route already. Someone with more experience moving batteries than I did when I started."

"You know their name?"

"No. But let me know what they're like," he says, checking the small device clipped to his belt. "Hm. Time's getting short."

Inge holds out her hand. Sylvester's grips hers like a vice. "I will," she says. "Can't let you get too comfortable."

As Sylvester stomps back up the entryway, he waves a hand over his shoulder at her. The badge on his collar winks in the light of the ship's lamps. "There's another three months until the next ship is due. Think about finding your damn ID card before then," he calls out. "Make a good first impression!"

From inside the station, Inge watches the ship part the clouds again. The sky on the other side is dim and bruised with sunset. Passing storms, Inge thinks, are things Sylvester would tell her about.

There are worlds out there where the sky is clear more often than grey, but if that were the case on Alacrity, she'd be out of a job. The sky never changes; little does. Inge gloomily watches the clouds for a while longer before moving off to find a chore to busy her mind with.

Nomads

Lauryn Hamilton Murray

nomad
/ˈnəʊmad/

noun
noun: **nomad**; plural noun: **nomads**

> a member of a people that travels from place to place to find fresh pasture for its animals and has no permanent home.
>
> a person who does not stay long in the same place;
> a wanderer.

*

As a decidedly unremarkable person, I spend an awful lot of time thinking about miracles.

Crazy ones, like that blind clairvoyant woman in Bulgaria who could predict natural disasters, or that girl who survived a 10,000 foot fall from a plane after it was struck by lightning over the Amazon rainforest. Ones you see printed as newspaper headlines like MAN WAKES FROM TWENTY YEAR COMA or CAT WHO CAN SMELL CANCER. And of course everyday miracles, like babies being born and winning the lottery and sunsets.

Then there's miracles like the fact my family has managed to not kill one another on what is now hour three of our six hour journey to whichever little red dot on the map my mother feels herself drawn to this time. She's in irritatingly high spirits, as she always is on a Move Day, driving with one hand wrapped loosely around the fluffy pink steering wheel while she uses the other to apply another coat of lipstick in a startling shade of crimson. I remember her nicking it from Debenhams. It's little wonder she insisted on carting Wolfie's pushchair around until he was about seven – she hid all manner of things in there. She stole a toaster once, wrapped it up in blankets while my little brother was perched on her hip.

As the smallest, Wolfie has been demoted to the middle seat, where he sleeps with his head on my shoulder. A snail trail of drool glistens down my arm. Wrinkling my nose, I place a finger underneath his chin and gently close his mouth.

Eddie sits on the other side, plugged into his Walkman. I find myself envying him as Mum's badly scratched Celine Dion CD belts out the same word – *baby* – on a robotic-sounding loop – *baby baby baby* – before skipping straight to the next track.

Ford lounges in the passenger seat, nose buried in his A-Level physics textbook. Despite Eddie being almost a foot taller than him, Ford insists that because he is the eldest he has the divine right of calling eternal shotgun.

We don't look related, my brothers and I. Ford is fair and wiry with neat, conker-brown hair. Eddie is handsome, his smooth skin a light shade of bronze, his head a mass of tight, dark curls. My own hair just about tips the scale from red into auburn, and the usual smattering of freckles on my nose and across my cheeks have since multiplied in the early spring sunshine. Wolfie looks like a cherub, what with his rosy cheeks and soft blonde waves. But despite our differences, we all have the same eyes. Mum's eyes. Pond green.

The four of us have different dads, you see. Remember that rhyme about Henry VIII's wives? *Divorced, beheaded, died, divorced, beheaded, survived.*

Think that, only in Mum's case it was more like:

Divorced, Dated, Died, Incarcerated.

Ford's dad was her waste-of-space high school sweetheart who she married at eighteen, then divorced several months later. Eddie's dad was a Nigerian exchange student who she had one date with and then never laid eyes on ever again. My own dad was killed during the Troubles. And as for Wolfie's dad, he is now, thankfully, a long-term guest of Her Majesty. Say what you like about my mother, but she sure knows how to pick 'em.

I finish a second packet of Wine Gums and read Ford's textbook over his shoulder for a while until the jumble of numbers and letters start to mess with my stomach. Well, *that* and the fact we are moving halfway across the country on another of Mum's whims.

In my almost sixteen years of existence, I have had nineteen homes. Nineteen and a quarter if you count this car, which Mum, Ford, Eddie and I lived in for a handful of weeks when the bailiffs decided to pop round for tea and biscuits. I have also attended thirteen different schools. I keep all the school ties, which Mum either nicks from lost property or buys second hand. One time, I tied all the ties together into a colourful snake just to measure how long it would be. The answer is just shy of twenty-two feet.

I've never been very good at friends. I've never had a boyfriend. I don't bother trying to fit in at school because I know I won't be there long.

My mother never stays in any one place. She breezes in, scatters a few seeds, but never hangs around long enough for them to take root.

'I'm a wanderer, darling. I go where my heart leads.'

And we, her reluctant offspring, are forced to follow.

She's mad, my mother. Mad, but also magic. I love and hate her more than anything in the world, and I'm still trying to figure out how that can be the case.

I let out a groan as the chorus of *It's All Coming Back To Me Now* is once again replaced by blaring static. Unfazed, Mum gives the stereo a whack and continues to sing along, loudly and off-key.

'Mum.'

'*There were moments of gold and there were flashes of light*—'

'Mother.'

'*There were things I'd never do again but then they'd always seem right*—'

I kick the back of her seat in impatience. 'MUM!'

'Yes, darling?'

'Put a sock in it, would you? You're giving me a headache.'

'I'm hungry,' announces Eddie, slipping his headphones off. 'What's for lunch?'

'There's Wine Gums, darling.'

'Not anymore,' I say.

'Pig,' mutters Ford from the front seat, not bothering to look up from his book.

I flick the empty packets at the back of his head. 'Fuck off, Twatford.'

'Don't tell your brother to fuck off, darling. Only I can do that.'

Beside me, Wolfie lets out a gigantic yawn. 'Mum, I need a wee.'

Five minutes later, we've pulled into a layby and all three of my brothers are standing with their backs to the road, pissing into a clump of nettles to the crescendo of *Halfway to Heaven*. When the song finishes, Mum swivels round in her seat to face me.

'How's my best girl?'

'Great, Mum. I'm having a brilliant time.'

'Don't be like that, darling,' she says reproachfully. 'This is a big day for us all. A change of scene, a fresh start, a new adventure. Isn't it exciting?'

'Oh yes. I can hardly contain my excitement.'

Mum fixes me with a shiny red smile. 'How about switching seats with your brother? Girls up front, boys in the back. How does that sound?'

'Pass.'

'Darling–'

'Leave it, Mum.'

'Bel.' She's still smiling, but I spot the tell-tale twitch at the corner of her left eye, and hear the ever-so-slight strain to her usual honey-sweet tone.

'Just piss off, will you?'

'*Belfast.*'

Remember when I said my mother was mad? So get this – what sane person names their children after the place they were conceived?

Ford's full name is Stratford. Yes, Stratford. As in *upon-Avon*.

The name on Eddie's birth certificate is Edinburgh, because that is where he had the misfortune of being unwillingly created. And because our mother is certifiable.

I have no memory of Belfast. Mum moved us soon after I was born, which was also around the same time my dad found himself on the wrong end of a semi-automatic.

Poor Wolfie got the worst deal of all, though. I mean seriously, tell me, because I want to know, what kind of mother calls their child *Wolverhampton*?

Well, mine, clearly.

The boys pile back into the car and we set off again, with Mum promising to stop off somewhere for bottled water and sandwiches. She keeps checking the rear-view mirror, and I know she's not watching the road or the other cars because the boot is packed so full of stuff that it's impossible to see anything out the back window. I look away at first when her eyes latch on to my face, irritated, but after a while I stare back defiantly, straight-faced and unblinking. The next time she does it I fix her with a maniacal smile that pulls a muscle in my cheek, winding up my middle finger like a fishing rod.

After an hour spent listening to a symphony of complaints – hunger, travel sickness, boredom, pins and needles – we join the queue of lorries turning off the motorway.

The service station smells like nappies and fried food. We sit on plastic chairs in a greasy spoon, Ford's head in his book, Eddie drumming his fingers on the table along to music I can't hear, and Wolfie licking all the salt and vinegar off the crisps before putting them back into the packet. Mum sips a black coffee, lipstick staining the rim of the mug. A few people peer curiously at us over plates of bacon and eggs or from behind newspapers all detailing the royal divorce, Lady Di gazing out dolefully from the front page.

There's No Place Like Home

Lucy Goodwill

The house is tall and slender, a little bit like me, with a black metal gate out front. It's in keeping with the rest of the street—a white exterior and a black front door—my one deviation is in the form of the knocker. From the road, you wouldn't notice it, so no risk of upsetting the neighbours. But once you get up close, you can see that it's a little golden bird whose tail you use as a lever to encourage the knock of its beak. There's something exciting to me about having a house that looks so perfectly ordinary on the outside, whilst you know it's anything but once you walk in.

On the other side of the door, you're led into an atrium, with a clear view to the top of the house through a winding network of stairs. The walls are a lush green, with intricate hand-painted details in all sorts of bright colours. Vibrant chains of flowers and vines curl across the surfaces, and by the staircase is a tree whose branches lead the way to the higher levels. The floors are all tiled so, if you wear the right sort of heel, the sound reverberates upwards, enticing you to explore the full breadth of the space.

The kitchen and dining room branch off to the left, the decor continuing the secret garden theme, all rich emerald velvets and soft, dusky pink cushions. The handles on every drawer are a sort of ornate golden leaf. If you continue upstairs, things shift as you reach the first floor—the living room and study. Both rooms have wooden panelling, painted in rich ochre. It's the closest I'll ever get to being surrounded by gold. My own personal version of a palace.

I don't keep many photos in this house as they seem to me to take away from the grandeur of the place. The few I permit myself sit on the desk in the study—ones of me and Mum and my brother Ollie and obviously one of my dog, Teddy. Occasionally, a picture of Ferdie sits front and centre, depending on my mood. I'll tell you about Ferdie another time.

Aside from the workspace, my favourite part of the room is an enormous, cosy chair with a matching footstool that I only ever use for reading. I like to feel swallowed by furniture as I'm transported into other worlds.

On the top floor is my bedroom, which spans most of the square footage of the house. I have the largest possible bed, which I cover in the softest furnishings and smother with oversized cushions, and a sheepskin rug to the side so I always wake up to softness underfoot. In this room, the colours are more sedate: pale blues and soft whites as though I'm sleeping amongst the clouds and not in a townhouse. The adjoining bathroom has walls the colour of deepest midnight, and in the centre I've installed one of those huge baths with a top that curls over and four free standing legs. Every night I climb in and scrub off the day, with only the light of a few pillar candles to see by.

For whatever reason, water often plays a part in my dreams.

The London house is tied with the seaside cottage for my favourite place. I've never assigned the cottage to a particular location, because all that really matters is that we're walking distance from the beach. By we, I mean me and Teddy. He's always with me here as

I know he'd love it best. The front of the house is painted white, like the other one, but it's shorter and fatter. The roof is bulbous, like the cap of a toadstool protecting the stem.

To reach the house, you either have to vibrate your way by car down a long gravel drive, or you can simply pop through the front gate on foot and follow five wonky stepping stones to the door. All the wooden fittings of the house—the outer window frames, ledges and door—are painted a silvery iced blue. Flower beds line the house's perimeter, and in the summer they overflow—a tiny sea of rainbows to greet each guest.

Out back, there is a garden, where Teddy and I spend a lot of our time when we're not walking the coastal paths and braving the sharp winds off the water. Every morning, we walk for miles, including a stretch of the beach where I pick up any shells or pebbles that catch my eye. Besides the sea, Teddy's favourite spots—and arguably mine too—are either the fireplace in the sitting room or next to the aga. Often after our walks we will vie for the same patch of the kitchen's floor slabs which borrow the warmth of the oven as the day wears on. Something about the sea air here makes me feel alive.

In Amsterdam, my boat is moored on the right side of the canal, not far from a bridge. The underside of the boat is a rich brown so dark it looks black, whilst the body of the ship is forest green. To make it a little more exciting, there's a strip of bright red paint around the helm, and the insides of the blinds are mustard yellow. In the summer, my friends and I sit on the front deck, surrounded by flower pots that I dedicated the spring months to tending, and we drink beer from green glass bottles. We people-watch and play a game of tourist or not tourist, with additional points granted if you come up with a compelling backstory.

On either side of the canal are seemingly endless rows of houses with brightly coloured fronts and contrasting wooden shutters. The colours of the buildings bleed onto the surface of the water, like streaks from Van Gogh's brush. Leaving his mark across the city, just in case you were to prioritise a visit to the Rijksmuseum over his. That said, the uneven nature of the buildings that line my part of the canal make me think more of Picasso. Better to live on a boat, I tell my friends—at least my home's not sinking.

I also use a boat to get to my Swedish summer home, which sits on one of the islands in Stockholm's archipelago. It has its own private dock which doubles as a diving board when I'm feeling brave enough to enter the water. The outside of the house is covered in wooden slats painted sunshine yellow. On warmer nights, Teddy sleeps under the bench at the back of the deck.

Every room in the house has floral arrangements, which sit in old glass milk bottles collected during previous sojourns. Each time I go into the city, I seem to pick up another trinket to add to the many shelves and surfaces, inexplicably unable to leave that old butter dish or dinner bell behind.

Set against a window in the back, overlooking the water, is the largest desk that I could find and, on top of it, an ornate antique typewriter. I escape to Stockholm every summer to write stories. Sometimes, I think I might manage a full novel, although if I'm aiming for that long a word count, I probably ought to reach for my laptop.

On days where I'm not so thrilled by the thought of intellectual isolation, I tend to dwell in a loft apartment in central Paris. It is owned by a rugged Frenchman called something like Jean-Pierre, my mysterious older lover who is, of course, also an artist. Somehow his decorating style makes it both metropolitan and rustic, with dark wooden floorboards that creak despite their weight and white walls the texture of sandpaper. The space is bare, but Jean-Pierre tells me that you don't need paintings or photographs when you have a view of the river so readily at your disposal. I'm inclined to agree, given the outer wall is made almost entirely of windows, but it does seem a strange position to take as an artist.

Jean-Pierre doesn't seem to believe that much in furniture either, because the only item I can picture is a cast iron bed frame. Though this probably says more of what I think about Jean-Pierre than it does of his design skills. On reflection, that dream isn't about the space and more what occupies it, so perhaps it's best if we move on.

Ah, I can hear Mum's footsteps on the stairs, so ... maybe not. Honestly, I could do this forever, if it weren't for the inevitable turning of my door handle.

Some Restraint

Nadine Brito

Tap. Tap. Tap.

The black cane that Mr. Wells clutches echoes on the mosaic tiles as he leads Liz towards the grand piano in the centre of the room. His raspy voice rattles off details about the make and history, but Liz doesn't hear. How can she focus when she's in front of the most beautiful piano in the world?

A Sauter grand, made of the finest chocolate-brown walnut, with intricate gold florals adorning the cabinet! And the ivories, the most immaculate shade of white! A gorgeous instrument backdropped by a panoramic window with a vista of the deep blue shades of Stewart Lake, small patches of green starting to appear across the way. The fingers of her left hand strike the air beside her, itching to play. She can't believe her luck. The perfect piano, in the perfect place, ready for the perfect song.

"I must say, Miss Shiels, it will be quite wonderful to hear music again." Mr. Wells clears his throat, bringing Liz out of her reverie. That, and his use of 'Miss'. She had already told him twice to use 'Ms.' But with the Sauter in the mix, he's forgiven. And seeing the precarious way he leans on the cane, a sheen of sweat on his wrinkled brow, she doesn't have the heart to remind him.

"Of course. Should I call Mrs. Johnson?" The live-in housekeeper is letting them be, but Liz is certain that she's waiting outside the room. She had probably moved the wheelchair out of sight.

"What would I want with that spying bat?" He purses his lips, wrinkling his crooked nose. "I'm not senile, despite what her and my idiot nephews seem to believe."

"Of course not, sir, I didn't mean to imply that."

He clears his throat again. "But my dear, let's speak of your music. What are you composing?"

Always that question, the one that seems so open and so shut at the same time. The one that she always struggles to answer, no matter the composition. The exact question Geoff asked before he left on his trip.

"I suppose I'm trying to figure that out," Liz answers, "for my thesis. It's almost done, but some parts aren't working, and I can't figure them out on my piano. It needs repairs." She doesn't tell him about the mouse that got in their duplex when Geoff left the door open. Somehow it had gotten trapped inside the instrument and had tangled itself in the piano wire trying to escape. The repairman said it would be cheaper to get a new piano.

"I hope that the beauty of this place inspires you, as it always has me."

"I'm certain it will. How long have you played, Mr. Wells?"

"I'm not a pianist!"

His voice snaps these words like an angry snake about to strike, his eyes flashing. Liz takes a step back, startled.

"I'm sorry, sir! I didn't mean to offend, I asked because of the Sauter..." Her mind races as she tries to figure out what caused such offense.

"Miss Shiels, please."

His voice is raspy again, his pale wrinkled face as dull as it was before. She watches him take a couple of steps to the mahogany desk along the wall, the black cane thudding on the tiles. Liz shakes her head, baffled. She can't have imagined his anger, she's sure, but if he's carrying on as normal...

"You may compose and practice anything you like during your stay here, Miss Shiels. However, before you do that, I wonder if you might play this song?"

He takes a silver key from the front pocket of his overcoat, holding it between his index finger and thumb, the aged stump of where his ring finger used to be as white as the piano keys.

Immediately, Liz understands his anger, and she shakes herself for her lack of tact while he unlocks the top drawer of the desk. From it, he pulls a few sheaths of paper, yellow and worn. Though the paper is old, the inky black music notes are vivid, visible to Liz from where she stands.

He holds them out to her. "Come here, dear. This is the song."

The song. Something about this intrigues her. Pushing all uneasiness aside, she takes the pages, glancing at them. It's curious that the song is handwritten. Other than her own work, she hasn't played non-printed music in some time. The penmanship is magnificent. She likes the delicate way the notes dot the staff, their tails in various bars trailing off with a flourish. The song itself reads as beautifully haunting, reminding her of *Moonlight Sonata*, also in C-sharp minor.

Clearing her head, Liz sits at the piano bench, placing the

sheets one next to the other on the music desk. She's ready to play, but as always, she pauses for a moment, her hands resting on the keys. There's something sacred in that quiet stillness before the start of a song that she always feels a call to acknowledge: that one moment of pure, unharnessed energy, all in one place, on the precipice. She sighs and lets her fingers fall into the keys, beginning the song.

All sense of time leaves her as she plays. All that exists is the piano, the notes in front of her, and the music. The melody flows as she expected from her initial reading, but some of the tonal shifts unnerve her in the way they creep up. She can't quite put her finger on it; it's a lovely song, well-constructed, but still, it feels ... off. A promise unfulfilled. *Too sudden, too incomplete* is her feeling as she reaches the final cadence. She holds the last chord, listening to its sad tone echo through the room. It stretches on and on, filling the space, searching for an escape, and she feels an overwhelming sense of hopelessness.

Free me!

The words are a roar in her ear. Suddenly her mind is overcome with only those words. They're all that she can hear as they repeat, over and over, in a woman's voice that echoes with desperation and urgency. And there is rage: a rage that pulses, pushing away every other thought of rationality that Liz feebly attempts to smother it with. Her head pounds and she gasps, letting go of the keys.

The words and the pain disappear as quickly as the piano falls silent. Liz shakes her head in a daze. Those final bars ... what the hell was in them?

"You play beautifully, my dear."

Liz is startled to see tears rolling down the old man's face, as if he didn't notice her gasp, didn't hear the horrid words.

"Sir, that's—that's very kind." She's alarmed to see the way his knees bend, his legs trembling as now both hands clutch the cane, holding on for dear life. "Why don't you have a seat for a moment?"

Rising, she goes to the desk and pulls its chair closer to him. He collapses into it, taking deep breaths. "Do you want me to get Mrs. Johnson?"

He grumbles in response. She falls silent, watches as he takes a handkerchief from his pocket and wipes his face, wondering what this song means to him. He clearly didn't experience whatever the hell she did. He went to a place of lightness, a place better than here, and now he's been pulled back to the reality that she's only too relieved to find.

"I look forward to hearing what you compose during your stay, my dear." His smile is warm, meeting his eyes. "I'm sure it'll be brilliant."

"I certainly hope so sir, I—"

"—do you think that you could play this song again? Once per day. Only after you're finished working, of course."

It's not a request. His statement is firm, direct. Non-negotiable. Liz can refuse; she's a paying guest, after all. But she has a feeling that Mr. Wells would have no qualms about making the rest of her week miserable if she did. His nephews may be the ones renting out her room, but they aren't here, and Mrs. Johnson doesn't seem to hold much authority.

Really, she has no valid reason to refuse to play one song. It's only a song, after all. Sometimes, it's simply a matter of music taking one's mind to different places. In this instance, it was a strange, dark place. Maybe it was a one-off, and that place won't exist next time. Or if it does, she'll know to expect it.

"Certainly, Mr. Wells. I'll play it again tomorrow."

"Most excellent, my dear." He coughs before grinning at her again, reaching out to pat her hand which rests on the desk. His pale hand is cold, with blue veins and wrinkles jutting out from all angles. His long, thin remaining fingers reminding her of the legs of a spider. She doesn't know why, but the image of the mouse in the piano wire flashes through her mind.

Pulling her hand away, she excuses herself.

Ghost Town, USA

Lily M. Frenette

Elizabeth Maron can't visit the playground regularly; sometimes she has a business meeting, or her husband invites her to a late lunch, or she just can't muster up the will to go. When she does visit, she brings a bouquet of daisies and sits on the last swing to the right. The moms have gotten used to seeing her, a tall and tidy woman, gray hair, and a chic outfit walking a straight line to her destination while their kids weave through the park screaming, hair wild from play. Every day, at exactly 3:52 pm, a small Glow comes running towards the park from Elm Street. If Elizabeth wanted, she could follow him from her old house the next street over on Cherry, but she always waits at the playground.

The Glow passes only inches in front of her before settling on the swings. If she wanted, she could reach out and touch the back of his head; hair that used to be brown and soft is now only a shimmering green, almost transparent in the bright light. There is a faint outline of Big Bird's smiling face on his shirt, and the pockets of his cargo shorts bulge with the pretty rocks he had picked up earlier. He sits for a moment above the bronze plaque she had installed last year.

The city allowed only this small notice, too worried that no one would want to play here otherwise.

Evan Maron

1989 – 1992

Beloved, joyful son

He turns his head back, looking to where she used to stand, and then starts to float back and forth. The swing remains still.

She doesn't usually stay the whole time, just the first ten minutes or so, until Evan flops gracelessly from a foot up onto the spongy surface of the playground and runs over to where she stood to hug her knees. She can deal with ten minutes—any more than that she can't focus the next day.

When the Glows first appeared, she wasted entire days following him around, waiting for him to flicker in and out of sight. His childish memories weren't strong enough to last him for the full day. She could only sob, and her friends would have to call her husband to pick her up. Now, she can do ten minutes and still drive home to spend the night with her family.

After Elizabeth leaves, or if she hadn't made it that day, the kids point and whisper at the Glow. It's a common dare to see who can swing in Evan the longest. Timing their movement to his back and forth can be tough—dealing with his memories, the sound of his mom singing and his absolute joy at being so high up, is an added challenge—but Zach Nelson, eight-and-a-half-years-old, currently holds the record with one minute and forty-eight seconds.

It took Zach four months to steal the record from Claire Charles, but he worked hard. There's a Glow at his house, an old man who knows words like "musket" and "woolgathering." Zach practiced moving about in him to gear up for his run. The first few tries were jarring; suddenly he was big, worrying about the heating bill and tax season, things that Zach had no idea existed beforehand. Then the man would move, and Zach would be left shivering on the sofa. His mom yelled when she found him like this, said it wasn't respectful. He couldn't let that stop him though; he just got better at sneaking.

Soon he was a natural, feeling the stretch of legs coming on and moving with them. There was a buzz on his skin when he was in a Glow and his body wanted to stay within it. He had already mastered swinging and was eager to go for the record. One word and everyone was whispering about it in class the next day—Zach was going to swing. Once Ms. Maron left, he strutted confidently to the swingset, hopping on while Evan was at the highest part of his arc. His friends came running over and the small crowd watched as he gained height, falling in and out of sync until they were moving in dual motion.

The other kids started counting, softly at first, gaining volume the longer he went. He heard them as if underwater. Evan's memories were weak compared to the old man, so Zach was still able to see through his own eyes. Flickers of the past overlapped with the present. Evan's brothers, Danny and Clay, were taking turns on the slide. After the playground, Mommy was going to take them all out for ice cream. Danny laughed at the hot burn of metal when he slid to the end, then he bounced up and sped past a set of girls Zach knew from summer camp playing Concentration. Mommy yelled out, "Be careful!" and he could feel her hand on his back as she pushed him up, up, up into the clouds. He squealed all the way back down.

One minute-ten seconds and he was past Claire's record; they cheered as he kept going. Zach only faltered when his mom, screaming and scattering the kids, yanked his chain to a halt and wrestled him out of the seat. He could've kept going for much longer.

Moira tried to be a good mom. She did everything right. Discipline was firm but loving; imagination was encouraged; hugs were plentiful. Yet Zach was to trouble like moth to a flame. She'd been chatting at the benches with the other ladies when Hannah, Luke's mom—how she ever raised such a sweet boy, Moira would never know—pointed a long, manicured finger at the swingset.

"Is anyone even allowed to use that swing? Someone needs to go collect their child." Her laugh tinkled. "Thank the Lord, Luke knows better than to interrupt a Glow on its mission."

Sanctimonious bitch, Moira thought before craning her neck to see who was going to receive the terrible parent award.

"Oh, isn't that your Zach, Moira? Such a shame."

Moira was sprinting towards the swings before Hannah could say anything else. She hadn't run since she tried to train for the elementary's FundRun 5K, and in the end she had just given money herself instead of participating. She bellowed Zach's name, but he didn't react. Now alerted to her impending arrival, a few of his crowd bolted. A core group remained, chanting higher and higher. She shoved past them, including a quite gleeful Luke, to grab hold of the swing.

Zach crumpled onto the ground once he was out of sync. He looked dazed for only a second before popping back up.

"I did it! Hah, I beat Claire!"

Moira, still screaming, reached out to shake her son, turning him away from his new fans to face her. "What the hell were you thinking? First Gary and now this poor boy! How do I get through to you that you're never supposed to go in a Glow?"

"But Mommy, Mommy I did it. I'm the bestest in the whole school now."

His words startled Moira. Zach wouldn't call her Mommy, only Mom, sometimes with a long o if he wanted an extra snack or to stay up late. She hugged him tight and whispered, "Don't scare me like that."

When she looked up, Hannah and the other moms were standing in front of the swings. Hannah's hand curled over the top of Luke's shoulder, and her smile dripped with superiority.

Moving to hold Zach at an arm's length, she put on her best tough mom voice. "No computer, no video games, and no texting your friends. For a week. Hopefully that will make you learn your lesson. And you have to tell your dad what you did when he gets home. And write an apology letter to Mrs. Maron."

"But Moooooom!"

"I don't want to hear it. We're going home."

Hannah held up her hands in prayer as they passed. "I'll ask God to give you extra strength tonight, Moira. You'll get through this."

If they weren't in front of a bunch of kids, Moira would've punched that smug grin off her face. Hannah was never going to get an invite to wine night again.

AUTHOR BIOS

Author Bios

Yasmine Bridge Originally from Leeds, Yasmine Bridge completed her undergraduate in English Literature at Newcastle University. For the past two years, she has worked with New Writing North, having her poetry published in their 2021 winter zine. Her poetry was recently published in the NCLA Anthology, Here and Now. Her debut stage play Bloody Hysterics, was produced in May 2022. She is currently the General Editor for The Inkwell and the Blog Coordinator for the Feminist Society.

Olivia Calderón is a Cuban American writer currently based in Edinburgh, Scotland. Having graduated from Florida State University in 2021 with a double major in Creative Writing and Classical Civilizations, her work strives to weave this background into the exploration of identity, culture, and the inner self.

Austin Crowley is a writer and actor from Connecticut, formerly based in Brooklyn, NY. He writes poetry, plays, and short fiction that tend to focus on the interior of the mind and mentalhealth. Two of his plays have been produced in NYC. His website:www.AustinCrowley.com

Alice Eaves is an interdisciplinary artist & writer from Northwest England. Her work is inspired by the human body as well as the nexus between the natural world and the current socio-political climate. She is currently enjoying writing about her Lancastrian heritage and old English folktales.

Kate Genevieve is a Canadian writer currently based in Edinburgh, Scotland. Formerly an elementary school teacher, she has a Bachelor of Arts and a Bachelor of Education from the University of British Columbia. With the desire of illustrating and investigating human relationships, she often draws inspiration from the many facets of interpersonal connection. Kate's writing is an evocative and unflinching exploration of sex, trauma, and the ambiguity of intimacy.

Alessandra Heitmann is an American poet currently living and studying in Edinburgh. She is originally from California and attended the University of Washington in Seattle where she studied writing and law. She has been previously published in the University of Washington's undergraduate literary magazine Bricolage, and has attended a creative writing workshop at the University of Chicago. Her writing explores themes of mental health and mental illness.

C.T. Hilton is an Edinburgh based poet, previously based in London, Paris, and Samos. He has a master's degree in philosophy, and within the field focuses on the commercialisation of authenticity, cultural capitalism, and postmodernism, all of which are motifs in his writing. His work has appeared in The Anarchist Milk Collective, Perception Culture, Existential FM, and Paris Lit Up. He has also written and published a cookbook entitled No One Cooks Alone.

Oona MacKinnon-Hoban was born and raised in Portland, Maine. She graduated from Barnard College, where she was a finalist for the Lenore Marshall Poetry Prize. She is also a recipient of the William Hunter Sharpe Memorial Scholarship here at the University of Edinburgh. Her work has previously been published in The Rising Phoenix Review.

Kinslee Sikes is a writer originally from Salmon, Idaho. She has a bachelor's in History of Art and Visual Culture from Boise State University. She currently resides in Edinburgh. Her writing is a synechdoche of contemporary culture as expressed through late stage capitalist, neo-romantic, hypo-realist values.

Tian Zehua 'Sarah' was born in Shanghai, China. She was a member of Fudan Poetry Club during her undergraduate years at Fudan University. She has published dozens of poems, some of which appear in High School Student Newspaper, Shanghai Literature, and Star Poetry Monthly. She writes bilingually and has published several English poems in 00's Poetry. In 2018, she published her personal poetry collection Three Bugs Under the Lamp. Her writing features a strong philosophical orientation and various explorations into life, nature and society.

Author Bios

Nicholas Alter is a writer with a passion for building immersive and imaginative worlds. His writing covers a wide range of genres, including literary fiction, sci-fi, fantasy, and magical realism. A San Francisco native, he obtained a BA in English with an emphasis in Creative Writing from the University of California Davis in 2016. In addition to his love of writing, Nicholas is also a trained acrobat, having received training from the San Francisco Youth Circus. He is currently working on his second novel.

Lily Bastock mostly fantasy fiction, but she'll occasionally write poetry. She has focused her literary studies on the late nineteenth and early twentieth centuries, looking mostly at gothic literature and the origins of the science fiction genre, within their Victorian England context. Her current work is a fantasy novel about pirates, assassins, magic, love, and loss. S Follow her on Instagram @lostfoxlibrary to keep up to date on her journey as a writer.

Rasika Bhale is a writer born and raised in India. She enjoys writing realist fiction, mythical fiction and magical realism. She maintains an occasional blog of short fiction and poetry on Medium. One of her poems was recently published in an Indian anthology titled *Daffodils*. She currently resides in Edinburgh. She is open to representation for her novella, *Shiva-Shakti Samvad: An Untold Ramayan*. It is an experimental retelling of the Indian epic Ramayana.
She can be reached at bhalerasika@gmail.com.

Raine Bracken is a writer and filmmaker from Toronto, Canada. She won Best Animation at TIFF Jumps Cuts for two consecutive years and in 2018 was a recipient of the Horizon Award for emerging female filmmakers. Her stories can be categorised as whimsical or murderous, although they often lie somewhere between the two.

Nadine Brito is a writer from Toronto. She has worked in the Canadian film industry for several years in various roles and was a co-founder of Toronto's Bloody Mary Film Festival (2016-2018), as well as co-head of Firecracker Writing Department (2020-2021). She loves any genre fiction involving magic realism, fantasy, and horror, and is currently adapting one of her feature screenplays into a novel. She holds a degree in Film Studies and Screenwriting from York University, and a postgraduate certificate from Humber College in TV Writing and Producing. You can find her online at unimpressed.ca or on Instagram @nadine_brito.

Charlie Chapman Born and raised in London, Charlie has spent the last few years moving steadily further North to pursue her love of fiction. After three torturous years of undergraduate Philosophy, she decided to dedicate herself fully to her writing, moving to Edinburgh for the MSc, and in the hopes of finally finishing a novel. Her writing often features fantasy, historical fiction and supernatural elements, and she is inspired by most anything dark or dramatic.

Jane "Connie" Coneybeer is an author from Glen Ellen, California. In 2022, she received dual honours degrees from Oregon State University: a BSc in Agricultural Business Management and a BA in English. Her piece "Lost & Found" was awarded OSU's 2022 Provost's Literary Prize for Prose and was published in Prism magazine. Her writing combines her experiences with agriculture, growing up in a large family, and a desire to tell stories, focusing on everyday life and the ways in which we treat those around us. Her works often look to uncover the human desire for a return to our roots from all walks of life.

Suzanne Enoch began her foray into the creative world in theatre and film, working as an actress, director and writer. She made this her career and successfully paid the bills this way for twenty years. She loves mixing the absurd with the mundane to create interesting mixes of literary genres.

Felix Foote is a short fiction writer from New York City. He has also lived in Manchester (UK) and Edinburgh. In 2020, he graduated from Bard College at Simon's Rock in Great Barrington, MA with a Bachelor of Arts degree in Creative Writing. He usually writes speculative fiction, such as supernatural and fantasy stories, and his work almost always utilises LGBT representation. One of his short stories was previously published in the short fiction anthology *Beyond the Veil: Supernatural Tales of Queer Love*.

Lily M. Frenette comes from Minnesota and was raised by the woods and waters. She writes at the intersection of nature, magic, art, and community. She enjoys working in multiple mediums, including: photography, painting, audio, video, printmaking, participatory experiences and crafting. Currently, she's at work on a novel called *Ghost Town, USA* about a town overrun by ghosts and tourists, a family torn apart, cults, art as therapy, and youth in revolt; she is open for representation. Lily graduated with a BA from Sarah Lawrence College. She works in Adult Education, volunteers with environmental organisations, and lives with the most fearsome cat criminal: Outlaw.

Lucy Goodwill is a disabled writer, artist and charity worker based in Edinburgh. Her writing spans fiction, poetry and creative non-fiction and explores subjects such as chronic illness, creativity and grief. Her work has been featured by publications such as 404 Ink, Dear Damsels and Popshot Magazine.

Charlotte Haley is a 24-year-old writer from Sunderland, UK currently based in Edinburgh. Her poetry has been published by Acumen and Scab Magazine, and her book reviews can be found on the University of Oxford English Faculty Library blog. She writes realistic short fiction with dark twists, often veering into horror. She has also written short films, one of which was produced by the BBC Arts New Creatives programme in 2020. Her favourite writers are Irvine Welsh, Shirley Jackson and Tsitsi Dangarembga.

Hazel writes in English and Chinese. With a background in history, a passion for non-fiction, and work experience as a journalist, Hazel aspires to be a writer of littérature engagée: to represent and change our social reality with the crystallised truth of fiction. Currently, her English stories often feature Chinese immigrants in Britain, which explores the experience of separation, integration and displacement.

Lauryn Hamilton Murray is a twenty-three year old Young Adult Fantasy author from Edinburgh, Scotland. She holds a first class degree in English Literature from the University of Stirling, and was the recipient of the John Drakakis Prize for the best performance in Shakespeare and Early Modern studies. Her short stories 'Pet Shop Girl' and 'Loving Silver' were published in the literary magazines No Parties and Kalopsia Literary Journal. Lauryn writes about complicated, rude and misunderstood girls, and explores the ways in which love, loss and loneliness can inform female identity.

Jason Philip Perlman is a software engineer and fantasy/science fiction writer from Princeton, New Jersey. His writing often centres on mystical creatures, magic and open universes. He enjoys exploring the potential of speculative fiction. In addition to his professional and academic pursuits, Jason is deeply passionate about storytelling and brings a unique blend of scientific and creative knowledge to his writing.

Zain Rishi is a writer from Birmingham, UK. He graduated in 2021 with a BA in Philosophy and Theology from the University of Oxford. After working as a bookseller for a year, he moved to Edinburgh to study the Creative Writing MSc. His writing explores experiences of cultural displacement and religious indoctrination. He enjoys writing in a range of genres, including realism, absurdism, comedy and horror. His poetry and prose have been published in Inkwell Magazine by PublishED. He is currently working on more short fiction and his first novel.

Anne-Marie Saich is an Edinburgh-born writer with an inclination towards science-fiction and anything weird or wonderful thanks to a childhood spent reading her dad's extensive collection of fantasy and sci-fi novels. Her previous work has largely been short stories, but she aims to finish a novella before the end of 2023. She has an MA in English Literature from the University of Glasgow. She can be found on Twitter at @SaichMarie.

Alison Schultz is from San Rafael, California where she grew up playing softball, basketball and volleyball before taking up rowing during her undergrad at the University of California, Santa Barbara. She now studies Creative Writing at the University of Edinburgh, where she plays and coaches volleyball. She spends her free time writing women's sports fiction and becoming best friends with every dog she meets.

Salvör Sólnes is a fiction writer from Reykjavík, Iceland. She graduated with a degree in Fine Art from Iceland University of the Arts. As a painter, Salvör spends a lot of time in the studio alone with her thoughts, and it is from those moments that her writing began. She works with the intersection of visual media and the written word. She is interested in how different languages approach meaning and has taken to writing fiction in English only recently.

Tara Troiano is a published poet, short story writer, and an agented novelist. She received her Bachelors of Art from The University of Texas at Austin and is pursuing her Master's at the University of Edinburgh. Her most recent publications include PEN America's 2022 college essay contest, Periphery Literary Magazine, and Cardinal Sins Literary Journal.

Sofia Reyes Valencia was born in Puebla, grew up in Dallas, and lives in Edinburgh. While she finds it hard to pin down her writing, her interests include history, comedy, and unhinged female protagonists. Not including previous script work and live performances at Monkey Barrel Comedy Club, Bedlam Theatre, and the Edinburgh Fringe, this will be her first fiction publication ever.

Sanna Waern Originally from Sweden, Sanna is a queer poet and aspiring novelist currently based in Edinburgh. She has a keen interest in LGBTQ+ literature and loves wild swimming, scruffy dogs, ghost stories and all things mythical. When not reading or writing, she enjoys gardening and rehearsing with her local theatre. Her work has previously been published by Sapphic Writers Collective and little living room.

Claire Wallace is a postgraduate student at University of Edinburgh. She was born in Los Angeles, California and spent the last three years in Japan teaching English. She enjoys travelling and exploring bookstores around the world. Her writing is inspired by the cities she has visited. She likes experimenting with different genres but is currently working on a series of urban fantasy stories. You can usually find her writing in cafes, especially when it is raining.

Xiaohui Yue's exploration in writing brought her from central China to the city of literature – Edinburgh. A strong believer of fluidity in identity, she writes in her second language to blur the linguistic and cultural boundaries that enclose a person's identity. Her writing edges on the verge of human imagination, in which she feels awed by the vast expanse and endless possibilities of the Universe, but also tethered by the deep-seeded humanity scattered around every corner on Earth.

FAS Team

9 781739 963538